# TRAINING TO MEET THE
# TECHNOLOGY CHALLENGE

## Latest titles in the McGraw-Hill Training Series

Details of these and other titles in the series are available from:

The Product Manager, Professional Books, McGraw-Hill Book Company Europe, Shoppenhangers Road, Maidenhead, Berkshire, SL6 2QL, United Kingdom. Telephone: 0628 23432 Fax: 0628 770224

# Training to meet the technology challenge

Trevor Bentley

McGRAW-HILL BOOK COMPANY

**London** · New York · St Louis · San Francisco · Auckland
Bogotá · Caracas · Hamburg · Lisbon · Madrid · Mexico · Milan
Montreal · New Delhi · Panama · Paris · San Juan · São Paulo
Singapore · Sydney · Tokyo · Toronto

Published by
McGRAW-HILL Book Company Europe
Shoppenhangers Road, Maidenhead, Berkshire, SL6 2QL, England.
Telephone: 0628 23432
Fax: 0628 770224

---

**British Library Cataloguing in Publication Data**
Bentley, Trevor J.
  Training to Meet the Technology
  Challenge.—(McGraw-Hill Training
  Series)
  I. Title   II. Series
  658.312404

ISBN 0-07-707589-7

**Library of Congress Cataloging-in-Publication Data**
Bentley, Trevor J.
  Training to meet the the technology challenge / Trevor Bentley.
    p.   cm.—(The McGraw-Hill training series)
  Includes bibliographical references and index.
  ISBN 0-07-707589-7
  1. Technology—Study and teaching.   I. Title.   II. Series.
  T65.B44   1992
  607.1—dc20

                                                      92-18445
                                                        CIP

Typeset by Book Ens Limited, Baldock, Herts
Printed and bound in Great Britain by Clays Ltd, St Ives plc

# Contents

# Series preface

Training and development are now firmly centre stage in most organizations, if not all. Nothing unusual in that—for some organizations. They have always seen training and development as part of the heart of their businesses—but more and more must see it that same way.

The demographic trends through the nineties will inject into the marketplace severe competition for good people who will need good training. Young people without conventional qualifications, skilled workers in redundant crafts, people out of work, women wishing to return to work—all will require excellent training to fit them to meet the job demands of the 1990s and beyond.

But excellent training does not spring from what we have done well in the past. T&D specialists are in a new ball game. 'Maintenance' training—training to keep up skill levels to do what we have always done—will be less in demand. Rather, organization, work and market change training are now much more important and will remain so for some time. Changing organizations and people is no easy task, requiring special skills and expertise which, sadly, many T&D specialists do not possess.

To work as a 'change' specialist requires us to get to centre stage—to the heart of the company's business. This means we have to ask about future goals and strategies and even be involved in their development, at least as far as T&D policies are concerned.

This demands excellent communication skills, political expertise, negotiating ability, diagnostic skills—indeed, all the skills a good internal consultant requires.

The implications for T&D specialists are considerable. It is not enough merely to be skilled in the basics of training, we must also begin to act like business people and to think in business terms and talk the language of business. We must be able to resource training not just from within but by using the vast array of external resources. We must be able to manage our activities as well as any other manager. We must share in the creation and communication of the company's vision. We must never let the goals of the company out of our sight.

In short, we may have to grow and change with the business. It will be hard. We shall not only have to demonstrate relevance but also value for money and achievement of results. We shall be our own boss, as accountable for results as any other line manager, and we shall have to deal with fewer internal resources.

The challenge is on, as many T&D specialists have demonstrated to me over the past few years. We need to be capable of meeting that challenge. This is why McGraw-Hill Book Company Europe have planned and launched this major new training series—to help us meet that challenge.

The series covers all aspects of T&D and provides the knowledge base from which we can develop plans to meet the challenge. They are practical books for the professional person. They are a starting point for planning our journey into the twenty-first century.

Use them well. Don't just read them. Highlight key ideas, thoughts, action pointers or whatever, and have a go at doing something with them. Through experimentation we evolve; through stagnation we die.

I know that all the authors in the McGraw-Hill Training Series would want me to wish you good luck. Have a great journey into the twenty-first century.

ROGER BENNETT
*Series Editor*

# About the series editor

Roger Bennett has over 20 years' experience in training, management education, research and consulting. He has long been involved with trainer training and trainer effectiveness. He has carried out research into trainer effectiveness and conducted workshops, seminars and conferences on the subject around the world. He has written extensively on the subject including the book *Improving Trainer Effectiveness*, Gower. His work has taken him all over the world and has involved directors of companies as well as managers and trainers.

Roger Bennett has worked in engineering, several business schools (including the International Management Centre, where he launched the UK's first masters degree in T&D) and has been a board director of two companies. He is the editor of the *Journal of European Industrial Training* and was series editor of the ITD's *Get In There* workbook and video package for the managers of training departments. He now runs his own business called The Management Development Consultancy.

# Introduction

This book is the result of many years' experience in creating training materials to be delivered to learners via computer technology. Using technology as a basis for learning calls for a range of skills that extend well beyond the normal training skills needed for conventional classroom-style training.

People responsible for creating training materials that are embedded, run concurrently with application software, or use technology as a basis for learning will find this book a useful guide. It will also be helpful for those setting out to develop electronic performance support systems (EPSS).

Technology-based training (TBT) is a very different form of training from the conventional 'taught' approach. In fact, it is not really training as many people understand it, but rather a way of presenting information so that those who choose to can learn from it. Using technology to produce continuous learning and support as an inherent part of the computer application means much more in terms of integration than conventional 'stand-alone' training. The principles involved are different and the approach to what to put into the material, and how to structure it, is quite unconventional.

When the computer is used as a means of delivering learning, the interactivity that normally exists between teacher and student is replaced by a predefined level of interactivity that goes far beyond pressing the space bar to view the next page. Creating such interactivity, and building programmes that offer the learner freedom and control of the learning process, calls for a new and fundamentally different approach to the design and writing of training materials.

The aim of this book is to describe and explain this approach and to put all the aspects of technology training into a simple framework that will link with existing standards and methodologies. It explains why the standards and methodologies are appropriate and shows how they produce the best results. In addition, the book provides a step-by-step guide to the key elements of technology training.

The book is organized into three parts. Part One covers the process of learning with technology, and deals with the critical issues of learning in an environment which can be seen as, but does not need to be, tedious, machine-controlled and rigid. The four chapters in this part provide a guide for you to build challenging, exciting, fun-filled and learner-controlled environments.

Part Two deals with the human/machine interface, and contains five chapters that show how the computer can be used to react in a very human and responsive way to the learner. Many computer-based training programmes fail to provide learners with choice and freedom in how they use the learning materials. This lack of choice spoils many well-conceived programmes and brings the idea of technology-based learning into disrepute.

The third and final part, 'The power of technology', provides a guide to utilizing the computer for learning in the most effective way.

In writing this book I have been particularly conscious of producing a practical guide that can be used by people who need to create the very best computer-based training. Each part has an introduction that gives a guide to the contents and use of each chapter in the section. Each chapter has been written in a particular format with an introduction, a discussion of the topic, a summary of key points, and a checklist for the practical application of the subject. The book also includes an index, and a set of practical 'user guides'—readers might find these summary sheets suitable for using as reminders of important aspects of the topic.

I have deliberately tried to avoid using the jargon that is associated with computers, but where I have felt it necessary to use technical terms they are explained in the text. I have tried to make the book as practical and useful as I can, and I hope that you find it a constant source of support.

*Trevor Bentley*

# PART ONE

# Learning with technology

# Introduction

The aim of all technology-based training (TBT) is to help people to learn. This means that the programme should feed the learning needs and desires of learners. Simply presenting a subject in an interesting way is not enough. People may learn from subject-centred materials, but many will not find it easy and will lose interest, and hence not learn.

To ensure that the technology is used effectively to enable learning to take place it is important to understand the learning process. The four chapters in this part provide a guide to developing learning-centred training programmes that make the best use of technology.

*Chapter 1    The principles of technology training*

The need for placing learning at the centre of the programme design and motivating learners to learn is explained. Technology is played down so that interaction can be seen as the way the programme responds to the learner, and not vice versa. The key factors in making programmes simple, non-patronizing, and able to provide meaningful and helpful feedback, are all covered.

*Chapter 2    The natural process of learning*

The basic process of learning is described with a clarification of learning freedom and learner control. The role of memory in the learning process is discussed and linked to the need for effective evaluation of learning through simulations, exercises and games. Context-sensitive learning is also explained in relation to the use of technology.

*Chapter 3    Supporting the learning process*

People learn in different ways, at different speeds and from different perspectives. I don't believe that we can force people to learn by making them follow a particular sequence. Our 'preprogrammed' approach must allow for greater flexibility in the way people use the material to learn. We should therefore attempt to 'signpost' the learning rather than force or direct it.

*Chapter 4    Technology learning: the barriers*

People seem to face a number of barriers when they come to use technology—technical, practical, psychological and human. When learning to use technology, or using technology to learn, these barriers have to be overcome.

The aim of this part of the book is to enable you to understand fully what happens when people use technology to learn. Feeding the learning process in an imaginative and flexible way is the aim of the training designer, so that no matter how many people use the programme they can all learn in their own way.

# 1 The principles of technology training

## Introduction

It is, I believe, important to start by spelling out the principles that are involved in successful technology training. Some if not all of these principles apply to other forms of training, but my emphasis will be on technology training.

This chapter sets the basis for all that follows. Good practice is based upon a set of principles that have been arrived at after studying the most successful practices of people actually learning and using technology in their daily work. The following quotation from Mao Tse-Tung explains this really well.

Go to the practical people and learn from them: then synthesise their experience into principles and theories: and then return to the practical people and call upon them to put these principles and methods into practice so as to solve their problems and achieve freedom and happiness.

Technology training can be summed up as 'helping people to learn to use technology'. If we believe that people learn best in an environment that is real and practical and which helps and supports them, then it follows that using technology to help people to learn to use technology is an obvious approach for us to take.

We can also use technology to help people to learn non-technology related subjects, but this is more challenging as we have to use the technology to introduce practical exercises and simulations of something which is remote from the technology. When we use technology to learn to use technology we have the very thing we are learning at our fingertips, and we can create real rather than simulated learning environments.

The development of multi-media with the use of advanced animated graphics, video and audio gives us the scope to use technology to create exciting and very real learning environments, but more of this later.

## Providing the most appropriate learning environment

Learning is a complex process which takes place as an interaction between learners and their environment. It is important therefore that in developing good technology training we concentrate on providing the most appropriate environment. This can best be done if the following principles are observed.

## 1   Technology training should be learning-centred

Training is learning-centred when the focus is placed on what the learner can learn rather than on the way the subject should be presented. The most logical way to explain something may not be the best way for people to learn. The idea that if we give people information, then explain how the information can be used, they will learn what we want them to learn, is a mispslaced and ineffective approach to training.

A great deal of computer-based training seeks to present learners with a sequence of 'things to learn'. These 'things to learn' have been devised by trainers from a study of the tasks to be performed. They are, in other words, the training designers' view of what needs to be learned. However, learners will each have a different interpretation of what they need to learn in order to perform the tasks. Rather than predict and then present a schedule of learning, training designers should build an environment which allows the learners freedom to learn what is appropriate for each of them.

When building such a freedom into programmes training designers have to have confidence and trust in the learning process. It is important to remember that we cannot force people to learn.

---

At a meeting with training designers I was asked to comment on the need to provide a structured learning sequence so that learners had to follow a particular path, learning each point in the logical order defined by the designer. My reaction was that even if the programme was structured in this way (assuming that the designer could create such a structure) learners would still decide for themselves whether or not to learn from it. Even if learners are denied choice in the way the programme is designed they will still exercise choice in whether to follow it. It is obvious to me that it is more effective to give learners choice in the first place rather than try to force them to learn in a certain way.

---

For a more detailed explanation of learning-centred training see my previous book in this series, *The Business of Training*.

## 2   Learning is voluntary and needs to be motivated

People learn when and how they want to. Presenting information and then testing people on whether they have remembered it is a very poor exercise in using memory. Memory is part of the learning process, but it is only a small part. It is like putting data into a database, testing to see if it is recorded correctly, and then never using it. People need to have a reason to learn, and that reason should preferably be a personal one. People are motivated to learn when they recognize that they can benefit personally from the learning.

If I start a training programme without first deciding what I want and/or need to learn, it is going to be very hard for me to learn. My interest may be stimulated by the material, but perhaps not in the way originally planned. I may well learn something from the programme, but not what the designer intended. Simply starting the programme off by saying, 'In this programme you will learn . . .' does not solve the problem; it may even worsen it if the learner is encouraged to prove the programme designer wrong.

---

In a programme designed for training bank managers to use financial accounts to assess the suitability of a business for a loan, the learners were given lectures about the meaning of financial statistics and the calculation of ratios. At the end of the learning they were given an exercise to assess a business based on the calculation of ratios. The success rate of the learners was very low. The programme was redesigned. The new programme started with an exercise that asked the learners what they needed to know to be able to assess loan suitability. When they had defined what information they needed they were shown how it could be obtained from the financial statements. The success rate at the end of the training was much better.

---

In the example above the reason for the improved success rate is simple. When learners know what they need to learn they will learn it even if the training they are given is very poor. If they don't know what they need to learn, even if the training is very good, they probably won't learn it.

### 3 Technology training programmes should be short, simple and success-oriented

As learning takes place through the interaction between learners and their environment it is important to ensure that they are given the opportunity to explore the whole environment, but to do so in short, simple modules that allow them to practise some task successfully, and then move to the next thing that interests them. It doesn't matter which order they go in. Some may want to follow a step-by-step sequence, others may want to dip in here and there, and yet others may want to experiment with their knowledge and skill. All these approaches are easier to deliver if the programme is built in short, simple modules that enable learners to be successful.

### 4 The technology aspects of the learning should be minimized

Many people find technology a threatening environment to work in. This is particularly so when people are learning to use technology. The technology itself should be played down. There shouldn't be any modules explaining how to use the technology, or trying to explain error procedures. These can be introduced gradually as learners start to interact with the environment. I recently looked at a computer-based programme for learning to use a keyboard. It was a very good programme in terms of its simplicity and its practical approach. Unfortunately, there were so many things to remember that it became a threat rather than a help to new users. Far better to find out what keys to press to do something, or what each key does.

**5   Learners should not be patronized either by the language used, or by the way the programme interacts with them**

Such comments as 'congratulations' or 'good, you got it right' when they have just selected the right answer from a list of four multiple choice questions is both annoying and distracting for learners. It is also very irritating to be presented with a page of text sentence by sentence as if learners can't handle reading four sentences all at once. This way of 'revealing' information is extremely patronizing, especially when learners have to press the space bar to get the next sentence.

In my experience I have found that most technology-based training contains too much information. Most learners are capable of using their own experience, knowledge and intuition to make connections and to interpret meaning without having every single aspect of the subject spelt out to them. From time to time learners may need to refer back, or to access some further explanatory information, but this can be provided as an option not as a necessary part of the training material.

Some of the best training materials present learners with a series of questions and the resources they need to find answers. Conventional technology-based training is rarely designed in this way.

**6   There should be a high degree of interaction between the programme and the learner, with the emphasis on how the programme responds to the learner and not the other way round**

The major concern of technology-based training designers is how learners will respond to different types of questions or tests. I believe this is not the main issue. The main issue in the interaction debate is how the programme will react to demands from learners. If learners want to ask for a further explanation, or an example or demonstration of the task, they should be able to do so at any stage in the programme. The programme should be able to react to the questions from learners. This approach to interaction is far more interesting from a design point of view, and produces much better learning environments than the typical and still all too common sequence of 'information', 'test', 'feedback'.

Lists of multiple choice questions and simple tests can be, and often are, a complete waste of time. Learners respond in a variety of ways from 'I must perform well' to 'What will happen if I do them all wrong?' The best way of allowing learners to check their learning progress, which is what we should be trying to do rather than 'test' them, is to present them with problems and exercises which call on them to use what they have learned to solve the problem. During this problem-solving process, they should be able to refer back to the training material for support. Unfortunately, many trainers see this process as one of cheating rather than supporting learning, usually the outcome of old-fashioned educational examination techniques.

**7   Provide challenging problem-solving feedback**

When interaction takes place it is all too easy to give a yes/no, or right/

wrong type of feedback. This is not only lazy, it is ineffective. Nor is it effective just to give the right answer. What is much more effective is to present a simple, or a complex problem, depending on the stage of learning, which challenges learners to think about what they are learning. If they want the answer to the problem they can request it together with an explanation of how this solution was reached. They should then be able to request a different problem to try out their new knowledge or skill.

# Key points

- Technology training should be learning-centred.
- Learners need to be motivated to learn.
- The technology itself should be played down.
- Interaction is about how the programme reacts to learners.
- Technology training programmes should be short and simple, and enable learners to be successful.
- Learners should never be patronized.
- Learners need challenging feedback.

---

### PRACTICAL APPLICATION

When designing and building technology training programmes the following practical things can be done to ensure the seven principles are followed.

- Allow learners to choose where they want to start their learning. This can be done by an initial menu of all the modules.
- Make it possible for learners to stop at any time and go back to the menu.
- Give learners the facility to access dictionaries, help, or other supporting material as they are learning, i.e. from within every module.
- Use the standards for writing training materials (see *The Business of Training* in this series).
- Time each module to last about 20 minutes or less.
- Give several examples from different viewpoints, e.g. the learner, the customer, the supervisor. This gives the learner a broader view of the task being learned.
- Use exercises instead of tests, and provide a range of exercises for learners to choose from.
- Don't tell learners things—give them the means to find out.
- Give learners encouraging feedback without being patronizing. If they have just completed an exercise successfully let them know it has been successful. If they have not been successful, suggest they try another exercise after reviewing the module, or offer them the answer to the exercise with the reasoning.
- Never give them the correct answer unless they ask for it.
- Because learning is voluntary you have to maintain learner interest. One way to do this is to throw in a few surprises. These can be a quick fun game, or a puzzle such as a crossword.
- Learning can and, I believe, should be fun.

---

# 2 The natural process of learning

We don't need to learn to learn. We are all born with the inherent ability to learn. We may need to be reminded from time to time that we have these inherent skills, but we never lose them.

We learn through a direct interaction between ourselves and our environment. We use all our senses of sight, smell, taste, touch, hearing and feeling. I include feeling because we often 'sense' things that make us feel good, frightened, happy, sad, etc. and we learn from these feelings.

We learn by using all our senses to take in information about our environment. The way we do this is very complex and the process is still not fully understood. We relate to our environment through experimenting and exploring. We try things out. We copy others. We trust our bodies to know what to do. When we first learn to ride a bike no one explains balance to us; we discover what it is by trying to ride and falling over. Eventually, our mind and body work out what balance is and we ride successfully.

## Learning

We all know how to learn. If you approach the design and building of technology training from the viewpoint that learners know how to learn, then it becomes possible to provide an environment which enables them to learn in their own way. There is a wide variety of different ways to learn, but I would like to describe four of the most common ways. If all these are catered for in the training programme then it will cover the learning styles of most people.

**Informed learning**   This learning style places the emphasis on concepts. Give me the information I need in a step-by-step logical sequence. I will remember this information, and then I will apply it in a simple exercise. If I fail I want to know what I did wrong so that I can reinforce the information in my memory before my next attempt.

**Experimental learning**   Here the emphasis is on trying out. Give me the basic tools needed, tell me what I am expected to do and then leave me to experiment. Give me more information and guidance as I ask for it. Tell me when I am successful.

**Exploratory learning**   places the emphasis on discovery and experience. Show me the final outcome, and I will then try to produce this. I will need to be given the tools and the guidance I ask for. I must be allowed to make as many mistakes as I am comfortable with. Encourage me when I am successful, or show me how to judge for myself when I am successful.

**Analytical learning**    This learning style emphasizes concepts and action. Show me the final outcome. Give me information about the tools that are used, and allow me to work out how the final outcome is achieved. Provide answers to my questions as I ask them. When I think I have worked it out I will need an exercise to complete. I will know when I am successful. If I fail I need more information, which I will ask for.

These four approaches need the same basic elements, but they are used in different ways with different emphasis. The basic elements are:

• information about the thing being learned to enable learners to conceptualize;
• examples of successful outcomes;
• information about how the successful outcomes are achieved;
• a range of exercises; and
• several examples of the thing being learned.

These can be placed in the programme in a sequence that the designers believe to be logical, but the elements should be in separate modules enabling learners to take the approach most suited to their learning style. In fact, the programme should encourage learners to approach their learning along any path they choose.

When we learn we do so through several stages: experiencing; reflecting on what we experience; developing concepts; and experimenting with what we believe we have learned. People go through these four stages in different ways and with a different emphasis.

# Memory

Memory is an important learning tool, but it is only a tool. The ability to remember something does not mean it has been learned. It is possible to remember many disassociated facts, but this is not learning. Learning is being able to use information that is remembered through understanding its relevance to our experiences.

If information is remembered in order to pass a test it becomes easy and tempting to delete it from memory very soon after the test. If information has to be used to perform some task in the form of an exercise it has to be understood, and so becomes learned. It is the application of the information within a meaningful experience in the learner's environment that causes learning to take place. In this case it is the information, the experience and its result which are remembered within the mind, body and spirit of the learner. This is what is meant by 'holistic learning'.

I have met people who have an excellent memory for all the ingredients that go to make up a good golf swing, without being able to replicate it in practice.

## Connectivity

When people learn, whichever approach they take, they learn by connecting the new information with things they already know. They make associations between the new information and existing knowledge and experience. This process has always been recognized by good trainers, who use analogy and metaphor to help learners make connections.

If learners are unable to make connections, the new information floats around in suspense. If it has no link to anything else learners are unable to relate it to their experience and so it becomes both difficult, and inappropriate, to remember it. If learners are given an experience first, and then the information, it becomes easier to make connections. Language is very important in this context. If the language being used is unknown to learners they are even less able to make connections than if the words are well known. This is a particular problem with computer technology.

## Sensory input

Because we learn with all our senses it is wise to optimize the sensory input by involving as many senses as possible in the learning process. How this is done depends on what is to be learned and the imagination of the training designer. It is always good to try to think about how all the senses could be stimulated in the learning environment.

When learning new technology it is perfectly feasible to involve the senses of sight and hearing. It might be possible to include touch through the keyboard or a touch-sensitive screen. Smell and taste are more difficult to imagine, but there could be situations such as chocolate manufacture where it could be relevant and practical.

## Experience

Optimizing experiental output is an important aspect of learning. Answering multi-choice questions involves very little experiential output. It is normally only a test of memory. The best form of experiential output is an exercise that replicates reality as closely as possible. This should provide learners with a challenging experience, both to assess learning progress and to further the learning. The closer the experience is to reality the better.

The development and use of simulations both as a form of demonstration, and as exercises, is an excellent way to give learners the opportunity to experience what they are learning. For those who wish to use the exploratory learning approach this is a very good place to start.

## Learner control

Research and experience have shown that we all learn in our own unique way. Though there are several learning styles, as defined earlier, in fact individuals find their own way to learn what they need to learn. Experiments have shown that if groups are presented with exactly the same learning experience, supported with the same materials, each member of the group will learn in a different way, and each will learn something different.

These differences have to do with existing levels of knowledge and experience, personality, background, physical capabilities, etc., none of which can be predicted by the training designer.

During the learning process individuals will choose what they learn, when they learn it, how they learn it, and how they confirm their learning. In addition they will exercise their learning choice, no matter how the training is presented and delivered. Learners are always in control of the learning they do, and they always exercise the freedom to learn as they want to.

**Learning paths**   However the training programme is designed, learners should be able to choose their own paths through the material. Some may want to follow the exact sequence offered by the training designer. Others may want to start at the end by looking at the final exercise and then work back through the material. The choice will depend on individual learning style, existing knowledge, etc. but the choice, whatever it is, should not be constrained by the training designer's own personal approach to the presentation of the material.

# Key points

- People don't need to learn to learn.
- People learn through direct interaction with their environment.
- There are four main learning styles: experiencing; reflecting; developing concepts; and experimentation.
- Memory is an important learning tool, but it is only a tool.
- People learn by connecting the new with the existing.
- Involve as many senses as possible in the learning process.
- Experimental output replicates reality as closely as possible.

## PRACTICAL APPLICATION

Trainers who accept that learning is a natural and inherent gift that everyone has can design training to optimize learning. This can be done as follows:

- Provide as much flexibility as possible in the way the programme can be used.
- Challenge the learners, both in concept and practical exercises.
- Don't spoonfeed them with information. Give them access to sources of information and let them find it for themselves.
- Introduce fun into the programme.
- Provide text, relevant visuals and sound wherever possible and effective.
- Introduce the programme with information about learners being responsible for their own learning, and provide a brief guide to the many ways the programme could be used, encouraging learner freedom and control.
- Provide a facility for learners to record what they have done and to make notes about what they have learned.

# 3 Supporting the learning process

Before writing this chapter I looked up the dictionary definitions for 'training', 'teaching' and 'educating'. All the definitions used active verbs such as to impart, to make happen, to coach, to communicate and to instruct. All of which implies that someone, i.e. the trainer, does something to someone else, i.e. the trainee. Teaching, training, education cannot 'cause' learning to take place as the dictionary definitions suggest. They provide an environment in which learning can happen. They help the process, but in no way do they 'cause' it to happen.

Supporting the learning process means providing learners with what they need, when they need it. When using technology this can be done if careful thought has been given to what learners' needs are. The learning-centred methodology (see *The Business of Training*) begins with an analysis of learning needs. This is an essential step if the programme is going to support the learning.

## Training needs vs. learning needs

There is a good deal of misunderstanding about the difference between training needs and learning needs. I believe that the difference is very important, and is a matter of perspective. Training needs are seen from the point of view of the training designers who work from the position of 'this is what we want people to be able to do, so this is what they need to be taught to be able to perform'. From this perspective the task is analysed and the knowledge, skills, etc. needed to perform are determined. These 'training needs' are defined from an 'external' perspective, usually employing someone who is already skilled in the task, the 'subject matter expert', as the source of information.

Learning needs are defined from the perspective of the learner. The task analysis is still necessary, but this time we use inexperienced people to look at the task and to say what they need to learn to perform it. The outcome is substantially different from the training needs analysis, and focuses on what needs to be learned, not what needs to be taught. There are situations where both training needs and learning needs are analysed and compared. This is particularly the case where safety is concerned, or where the task is involved and complex, and where inexperienced people would not recognize something which was important.

The learning needs, together with any additional training needs, are then used by the training designer to produce a programme which presents learners with the most interesting and effective ways of learning what they need.

In producing a training programme to meet learning needs the training designer has to be highly imaginative and creative in providing resources for learners that will enable the learning to take place. There is no particular formula that can be offered for how learning needs can be met, but it is worth discussing four of the main components of any programme, which are information, examples, exercises and guidance.

## Information

Learning usually involves the acquisition by learners of new information. This information may be specific facts, it may be explanatory, or it may be descriptive. It can be provided in a variety of ways. Information, in whatever form, is more readily assimilated if it is provided in answer to a question. When information is just given without learners having some context into which they can fit it, the result is puzzlement and confusion. They may hear the words and see the pictures, but they do not make sense. When learners have to find and sort out the meaning of information its relevance and value is considerably enhanced.

Information does not have to be presented in a factual logical sequential way, although this seems to be the most common way to do it. Information can be divided into blocks such as facts, process, meaning and context.

For example, in a training programme for 'opening a cheque account', the information could be prepared in blocks such as:

- Facts—what an account is
  —what a cheque is
- Process—how to open an account
- Meaning—why someone should want a cheque account
- Context—how a cheque account relates to other accounts
  —what cheque accounts can be used for

In this example some learners will never need the information in the facts block because they already know this, but the designer cannot assume this for all learners, so it is provided if it is needed. The rest of the information can be accessed and understood in any sequence in which learners care to do it. Even if someone who didn't know what a cheque or an account was looked at the 'meaning' information first they would still learn from it and could get the 'facts' information when they wanted to. Far too much information is provided on a 'let's cover everything' basis, and causes frustration, confusion, or both.

## Examples

Observation is a powerful learning process. It is possible to learn a great deal just from observation. I have tried a number of experiments with learners, just showing them something without any other form of communication. They then had to carry out the task.

The results have always been startling both to them and to me. People are able to learn to do things without knowing what they are doing, why, the names of the tools, the process they are following, or anything about the task.

I have similarly given detailed information to people about a task and I have watched as they struggled to make sense of it. As soon as they were given an example everything seemed to make sense.

Giving examples of a task at the very beginning of the programme helps learners to seek information, and to be able to fit everything else into the context of what they have observed.

## Exercises, simulations and games

Most people are very keen to have a go at something that they are learning. This may happen immediately after they have observed something, or after they have gathered some more information. The exercise might be a very simple one, which when completed successfully gives confidence to try a more difficult one.

There should be a wide range of exercises for learners to choose from. The choice gives them a feeling of control and also allows them to challenge themselves by trying harder and harder exercises. Some people like to start with the most difficult exercise and struggle until they succeed.

The exercises should be as real as possible and should ensure that learners gain the knowledge and skill necessary in order to complete them. Care should be taken to try to make sure that an exercise cannot be completed successfully just by a lucky guess.

Simulations are practical tasks as close as possible to the reality of what learners will be asked to perform. The objective is twofold:

• to provide practice in carrying out the task;
• to provide a means of evaluating learning progress.

Simulations can be very effective learning mechanisms, provided learners are fully supported and given timely and relevant feedback regarding performance.

Games are also an excellent way of providing interesting and challenging ways of exploring what has been, and is being, learned. These can be involved and complex, or simple puzzles such as crosswords. A great deal of our formative learning, particularly in social skills, came from playing games. Unfortunately, adults are presented with few opportunities to learn from games and the process of play.

In one CBT programme I designed, which was to help managers interpret financial results, I included a game for them to play which gave information about decisions that had to be made in a fictitious company. They had to advise the management on what to do and predict the outcome. The programme then calculated what would happen and gave them the results with reasons. It was a simple game, but all the managers reported how much they enjoyed it, and how much they had learned from it.

## Guidance

The training programme should have sufficient information to guide learners through the learning. This might be provided in the form of detailed 'Help' messages, or it might be a separate guidance module which provides options of where to go from wherever learners are when they seek advice.

The guidance module could be built in the form of a map with various paths depicted either graphically or using text. There could be a link with the training programme so that an arrow flashes on the map indicating the learner's current position. From this information learners could choose where to go next.

Another form of guidance could be built into each module of the programme showing learners the possible places they could go to in the form of navigating information, e.g. 'To return to the previous module press F4, to try an exercise press F6'.

If the programme is designed to support learners it will constantly provide signposts and directions so that learners will be able to steer their own path to learning.

## Support

In the learning context support means providing help and encouragement. For this to be effective it has to be done when learners need it and in a way that motivates them to continue.

Telling people they have done something wrong is not supportive. Not providing help 'because they are supposed to have learned it by now' is not supportive. It is not supportive to give difficult exercises without learners being able to choose simpler ones. Being challenging does not mean being unhelpful or unsupportive.

I interpret support in four main levels, but there are more ways of supporting learners than these four. Support is only limited by the designer's imagination and creativity. My four levels are:

- **Help** available at any time by selection, or in the context of what the learner is doing.
- **Examples** available whenever learners want to see an example of what they are learning. These can be called by selection from a menu, or in the context of what is being learned.

- **Guided performance**   carrying out an exercise with guidance from the programme.
- **Supported performance**   carrying out an exercise or simulation with the ability to call for help or examples, or switch to guided performance.

The most important aspects of support are:

- enable learners only to do things right; never tell them they are wrong;
- always provide some form of support;
- always use encouraging language without being patronizing; and
- training programmes are to help people to learn, not to 'catch them out'.

# Key points

- Teaching, training and education cannot 'cause' learning to take place.
- Supporting learning means providing learners with what they need, when they need it.
- Learning needs should be expressed from the learner's perspective.
- Information is more readily assimilated if it is provided in answer to a question.
- Observation is a powerful learning process.
- Most people are keen to have a go at what they are learning.
- Learners should be able to choose from a wide range of exercises.
- The training programme should guide learners through the learning.
- Support means providing help and encouragement.

---

### PRACTICAL APPLICATION

There are four main steps to take to provide effective learning  support.

- In the design phase of the programme development, prepare a map of the programme listing all the possible learning paths that can be taken.
- Using the programme map, devise all the signposts and navigating directions that need to be built into the programme.
- Ensure that the four primary elements of information, examples, exercises and guidance give learners a wide choice.
- Use the technology as a means of support for learners by utilizing the latest developments for accessing a wide range of information sources.

---

# 4 Technology learning: the barriers

Technology change seems to make many people apprehensive. I have met this situation time and again when I have been introducing new computer systems. Why should the prospect of technology change cause people to be apprehensive? I believe that it is partly because of the mystique which surrounds the use of computers, partly because of the feeling of not being in control, and partly because few, if any systems, have been designed to be easy to use.

People who understand the mystique, who have been initiated, and who have learned to control the machine quickly become 'systematized'. I divide these people into three categories: computer buffs, technicians, and those with 'gadget disease'. They have the effect of making every-one else feel positively useless. This feeling can be so strong that some people remove it by refusing to have anything to do with computers. People don't feel so bad about something that they have chosen not to do. For many people it is not possible to reject the computer in this way, and they have to face the prospect of learning to use the technology.

There are a number of barriers to learning to use new technology that seem to arise. Understanding what these barriers are can help trainers to build programmes that overcome the problems many people face. There are four main groups of barriers. These are technical, practical, psychological and human.

## Technical barriers

If trainers are involved in the early stages of the development of new computer systems, technical barriers can be removed before they become a problem. The four types of technical problems can be described as follows:

- the functionality of the technology, i.e. how the equipment and the system actually works;
- the limits imposed by the system;
- the speed with which the system operates; and
- the interface between the system and users.

**System functionality**    System designers concentrate, quite rightly, on the technical performance of the system. Ease of use, and the practicality of what they design,
often come some way down their lists of priorities. When I look at systems there are always many examples of this failure to consider the
needs of users. The answer seems to be to leave it for trainers to
explain the system functionality to users. This not only increases the
training burden, it also creates a barrier to learning.

Functionality is, of course, essential to the successful performance of the
system and the people who use it. The system must do what it is
expected to do, and it must cope with a wide range of options that
might be presented to it. This does not mean that it should be compli-
cated and hard to use, but this is often exactly what happens. The
functionality of the system is frequently requested by 'user representatives' who help to draw up a 'requirements specification'. During this
process two things happen. First, the user reps want to make sure that
they miss nothing out and, secondly, the designers come up with all
kinds of things that the system could do. This usually leads to the
design and subsequent building of a system that is far more compli-
cated, and has far more features, than could ever be learned or used.

Dealing with this problem of the 'all singing and dancing' system is
never easy, especially if it is presented to the trainer as a *fait accompli*. In
my experience, if trainers haven't been involved in the design they will
need to study the system and to simplify it before attempting to produce
a training programme.

---

In one example when I was advising a client about designing an HCI, I had suggested five aspects of the screen appearance that should be highlighted using
colour and reverse video. This was the limit before the screen became messy
and unusable. A system developer (a technician) suggested that we should consider adding some more highlighting facilities because the system had a list of
twelve different ways to do it. He seemed quite upset when we said we didn't
want to use them.

---

The best approach is for trainers to point out where the functionality
conflicts with ease of use and to seek to change the system to remove
such conflict. System designers are often unwilling to change their
design, but it is important to persevere and to ensure that the system is
as easy to use as possible.

**Imposed limits**    To ensure accuracy and security, there are many limits placed on the
way that systems can be used. These limits are necessary and have to be
fully understood, but far too many limits are placed on systems which
in reality are there to cover up inadequate and poorly conceived programmes. There is, however, another group of limits that are placed on
users by the way the system has been designed. This is often referred to
as discipline, or control procedures. This second category of limits is

purely to support what I consider to be poor design, e.g. the designer may have limited the space available for 'employer's name' to fifteen characters. The reason is the amount of space on the screen. If the employer's name is longer than fifteen characters the user has to find some meaningful way of reducing it to fit.

System designers will often complain about the limits that are placed on them by screen sizes, programming needs, and time and cost. Some of these complaints are justified, but there is no excuse for producing inadequate systems design to save money, when the cost of low performance will far exceed what might be saved.

For trainers the problem is usually to train people to work within the limits set, when a far better approach would be to examine every limit to see if it is truly necessary, or to check whether the design can be improved to remove as many limits as possible.

**Operating speed**

There are two parts to this problem. The first is the speed with which users respond to the system, and the second is the speed of the system's response to users.

Many users fail to appreciate that they are in control of the speed with which they use the system. This is made worse by designers who produce systems that appear to control what is happening, especially when there are many limits.

The speed with which the system responds will vary depending upon how busy it is at any one time. This seems to cause untold difficulties, with users 'waiting' for the system. People seem to find it difficult to be patient and to do something useful while they are waiting, even when the waiting is restricted to one or two seconds.

In most systems the operating speed at the user end is normally controlled by the activity the user is performing, and not by the speed of the system. This seems a very hard concept for system designers to comprehend. They seem obsessed with the speed at which the computer works, which can be very important when a large mainframe is expected to deal with say 10 000 transactions a minute. An excellent example of this can be seen in a travel agent. When people book a holiday the transaction can take anything from ten minutes to a couple of hours. During this time the computer is used spasmodically for a few minutes, with the actual booking taking a few seconds. During this process the central computer is probably handling thousands of bookings.

**The user interface**

This nearly always causes problems. The reasons are threefold: a lack of thought about the needs of users; a lack of consistency between systems; and poor ergonomics.

Users' needs can be summed up as ease of use, and comfort. Ease of use depends upon the design considerations about the ways that users work, not just in using the system, but also in dealing with customers, etc. Comfort is a factor of confidence, support and physical comfort.

Things like keyboards, space and screen layout come into this. And finally ergonomics, or the physical arrangement of the workplace: siting the screen at eye level, and placing the keyboard in a comfortable position, are essential requirements. Sufficient space for paperwork and proper seating are other key factors.

The human/machine interface is dealt with in more detail in Chapter 6, but for the moment I will simply say that this is one of the major barriers to learning to use technology, and one that reduces performance considerably.

# Practical barriers

When people are learning something new they need plenty of time and space in which to concentrate on what they are doing. In addition, they need a supportive environment and they have to want to learn. How obvious, you might think—is it really necessary to discuss such things here? Well, as these four elements are frequently missing when people are asked to learn to use new technology, I think the answer is a resounding *yes*. Funny, isn't it, how the obvious is nearly always missed?

## Time

There is nothing worse than not having enough time to learn something. Learning under the threat of an unreasonable deadline is counterproductive. There has to be some timescale for the learning, but it must be realistic and carefully planned. When time has been allocated for learning it should only be sacrificed for the sake of the current work when it is essential to do so.

There is a great temptation to minimize the time needed and to play down the importance of the learning. Consequently, many new systems are introduced when people are only partly trained and lacking in confidence and competence.

This is not to say that training should be long-winded and time-consuming—far from it. I believe that training can be simple, carried out in small steps, and of short duration. Some of the reasons why technology training seems to take so long are set out in the first part of this chapter.

## Space

Space must be made available for the learning to take place. One terminal perched on the end of a desk in the corner of the office is not adequate. Nor is it conducive to learning to have a bank of terminals in a training centre, where people are under the scrutiny of their peers. What is much better is a special area equipped in the same way as the workplace, but with additional space for a supervisor to sit with the learner. If this is in a training centre then each position should be screened from the others.

Learning in the workplace itself is probably the best approach if it is done effectively, with people being given the appropriate time and space in which to learn. In one example the staff learnt at the work position with a notice telling customers who approached that the person was undergoing training to improve service. This gave the learner the time and space necessary, improved customer relations, and increased everyone's confidence.

**Environment**    A good learning environment is fully supportive of learners. Supervisors and managers should place the utmost importance on the learning, and give time and space for it to take place. They should encourage everyone to treat the learning seriously, and yet enjoy it. Perhaps the best learning environment is the normal workplace where learners are fully supported and helped by colleagues and supervisors.

Sometimes this is not possible and special learning environments have to be created to provide learners with a safe and protected method of learning. Simulators for airline pilots is one example. In such instances, effort should be made to ensure the learning environment is as close to reality as possible.

# Psychological barriers

The prospect of learning something new causes apprehension because:

• people are dealing with something new and strange;
• they feel inadequate and unprepared;
• they don't know what to expect; and
• they have heard rumours about difficulties and problems.

For some people this prospect may generate a feeling of being challenged, a feeling of excitement. For others, anxiety may cause physical symptoms of illness. This will naturally depend on an individual's make-up and past experience and conditioning.

From a training point of view these problems have to be dealt with at the very outset, or the people concerned will never reach the stage where effective learning can take place. There are, I believe, five critical psychological barriers that have to be removed, and this is true of all forms of change:

• fear of the unknown
• self-doubt, particularly in respect to the question 'Will I be able to cope?'
• fear of ridicule
• negative motivation
• fear of failure and censure

**Fear of the unknown**    All humans fear the unknown, to varying degrees. This fear is based on an anticipation that all might not be well, that there might be some disturbance to their comfort or security, both physical and mental. This feeling is evidenced by the comment many people make after experiencing something new: 'It wasn't as bad as I thought.'

**Self-doubt**    From the very beginning of their lives people are constantly given incorrect information about themselves. Much of the information is negative. People are told they are stupid, they are naughty, they look a mess, their hair needs cutting, and so on. This builds a strong negative attitude towards themselves. When people are faced with some kind of challenge, all these negative thoughts surface and they doubt their ability to cope.

**Fear of ridicule**  Everyone has a strong sense of belonging. This is reflected in the need people have to be accepted by a variety of peer groups. This acceptance is important to them, and to be accepted they have to be equal or similar to their peers. To be different generates ridicule, and could lead to rejection and isolation.

**Negative motivation**  To carry out any activity, people need to be motivated. This motivation could be either positive, i.e. they want to do it, or negative, i.e. they don't want to do it, but they will to get it out of the way. When people are negatively motivated they do the minimum necessary and they learn very little, hoping they will never have to do it again.

**Fear of failure and censure**  Many people have learned that failure is a sign of weakness and will lead to ridicule or worse. A very competitive educational environment increases the fear of failure and the consequent censure. Many people, therefore, are hesitant about trying new things in case they fail.

# Human barriers

People get in the way of people learning. As trainers we might not like to accept, or admit, this is true, but it is. I feel that people create barriers to learning through four distinct aspects of human relationships:

- communication
- caring
- ego
- personality

**Communication**  This is a crucial barrier to learning. People, especially those concerned with computer technology, are not good at communication. This is true for all aspects of communication. If I pause and consider the four parts of communication—message construction, transmission, reception and interpretation—we will be able to assess the possible extent of the problem.

Frequently, the message we construct is too long, too complex, and has no basis of connection in the current perception of listeners. Unless the message is simple, short and specific there is little chance of getting it across. The language we use is also important if we want to convey our message successfully. The key is to concentrate on short, simple sentences, using small words and avoiding jargon.

Trainers are supposed to be good at transmission of messages. We learn how to use all kinds of techniques including visual aids, but we persist in using methods, such as lectures, which are notoriously ineffective, especially for technology-based subjects.

The reception of the message depends on the ability and desire of the recipient to listen. This ability and desire is frequently not present, is not encouraged by trainers, or is simply ignored and assumed to be happening because the trainer is speaking.

Interpretation of the message demands that the listeners have some existing basis of knowledge on which to make connections. I remember an occasion when a computer person was asked to explain what a 'byte' was. The questioner had no idea what it was. The computer buff answered that a byte is eight bits. The questioner had no existing basis of knowledge to help her make sense of this answer.

**Caring**     Unless trainers care about the learning they are trying to help take place, and unless they care about the learners, little effective learning will happen. When learners sense that trainers don't care they cease to care themselves about what is happening. Sometimes, trainers mistake enthusiasm for caring. Enthusiasm is important, but enthusiastic trainers have little patience with those who do not respond enthusiastically. Caring is quite different. It involves helping people to learn, including those who don't appear to want to, or who are afraid.

**Ego**     I was tempted to put this heading in capital letters so that it stood out in the same way that the ego of many trainers stands out. What is it about standing at the front, in charge, the one with the knowledge, that turns people into pumped-up dollops of ego? Sometimes ego can help by boosting confidence, and trainers need confidence, but when it gets out of hand learners just switch off. Perhaps the worst thing that happens is that learners hand over the control of their learning to the trainer, and by doing so they stop learning.

**Personality**     There are some people that I just cannot learn from. It might be the voice, the way they stand or behave, the way they respond to my questions, their odour, or any of a multitude of things that I group together under personality. Whatever it is that puts me off, it completely blocks my attempts to learn. Other people may not be affected the way I am, and it is not the fault of the trainer, but nevertheless it is a barrier to my learning.

# Key points
- The four groups of barriers are technical, practical, psychological and human.
- The technical barriers are:
  —extensive functionality;
  —the limits imposed by the system;
  —the speed with which the system operates;
  —the interface between system and users.
- People need time and space and a supportive environment in which to learn.
- Learning something new causes apprehension.

- The five critical psychological barriers are:
  —fear of the unknown
  —self-doubt
  —fear of ridicule
  —negative motivation
  —fear of failure and censure
- The four human barriers are:
  —communication
  —caring
  —ego
  —personality

---

### PRACTICAL APPLICATION

There are four steps to take in order to establish and understand the barriers to learning in each specific case. These are:

- Prepare a statement of the anticipated barriers using the four headings of technical, practical, psychological and human.
- Study each of the barriers and discuss them with everyone involved, particularly with the potential users of the new system.
- Assess the implications that the barriers will have on the learning, and the implementation of the new systems. This is so that a case can be developed for the removal of the barriers.
- Prepare a report on the effects that the barriers will have if they are removed, and recommend that time is spent in establishing cost-effective ways to remove the barriers.

# PART TWO

# Building the human/machine interface

# Introduction

This is perhaps the crux of meeting the technology challenge. No other single factor plays such an important part in the ability of people to learn to use technology effectively, and yet no other factor is so poorly handled.

In this section of the book I look at those aspects of the human/machine interface that trainers can influence. This influence is more extensive than many trainers recognize, either because they have been prevented from getting involved at the right level, or because they have not believed they have the knowledge and skill to have any impact at all.

The five chapters in this section cover the human/machine interface from three different perceptions. First is that of the user, second the trainer and, third, the system designer.

### Chapter 5    Overcoming technology learning barriers

This chapter concentrates on removing, or reducing, the barriers described in Chapter 4. The suggestions made here are all possible and practical, and have actually been used to improve the human/machine interface so that learning could take place painlessly, with interest and enjoyment.

### Chapter 6    The human/machine interface

Defining any subject is likely to create disagreement, but nevertheless I have attempted to define the human/machine interface in terms of its relevance to learners and trainers. It is necessary to understand the technical implications of what I suggest, but this is far easier than many trainers think. Trainers are not necessarily going to *build* the interface, but they can influence its design.

### Chapter 7    The effective use of language

One of the key elements of the human/machine interface is the language that is used to communicate with the user. The majority of system designers still treat the user like another part of the system. They try to program them to respond in exactly the desired way, and they try to do this using the same kind of language that they use within the computer. They see no place for politeness, patience, tolerance or choice, and this is clearly reflected in the fractured language that is used.

*Chapter 8    Understanding and communication: the role of analysis*

When people learn, they go through a process which is rarely described as analysis but which does, in fact, closely represent analysis. In this chapter I describe this process, and show how the understanding of the process can help trainers to define and design the most effective human/machine interface to enable learning to take place quickly and effectively.

*Chapter 9    Continuous learning*

Training may stop, but learning never does, at least not while we are alive. This is where trainers have to ensure that, once the formal training is over, users can continue to learn from using the system. The creation of supportive systems is very important—the principles are covered in this chapter and Chapter 13 describes how it can be achieved.

This section of the book should enable you to gain a better insight into how trainers can influence the design and construction of effective human/machine interfaces that make systems easy to use and easy to learn.

# 5 Overcoming technology learning barriers

Perhaps the best way to overcome any barrier is to remove it. When this is not possible the second approach is to go round the barrier, the third approach is to reduce it, and the final approach is just to go through it as if it wasn't there.

## Removing technical barriers

The four types of technical barriers described in the previous chapter can all be removed, or overcome, by analysing the system from the point of view of how the job is to be done, rather than how the system works. This really means shifting the emphasis from system functionality to system usability.

---

I was working on one major project where the designers had suggested that when a customer account was being opened the teller should enter the customer's marital status in one of six categories: M—for married, S—for single, W—for widowed, D—for *de facto* (living with someone else), X—divorced, L—separated. The designers had not considered how the teller might actually get the information from customers without offending them, or being physically abused. We changed the system so there were three categories: M, S and O—for other.

---

Many trainers will be familiar with 'structured task analysis', where the job to be done is broken down into detailed tasks, for each of which there is a declared competency target. If this approach is followed it should be possible to study the system and to suggest ways in which the technical barriers identified can be overcome. It will help if systems designers are following agreed user interface standards, and it also helps if writing standards have been followed in terms of the use of language, etc.

## Extensive functionality

Extensive functionality can be overcome by looking at the priority needs for performance to reach competency levels, and then removing all the other facilities that do not directly aid performance. If this is not possible, or if the resistance is too strong, then design the training to ignore these seldom-used facilities. In most cases, performing 99 per cent of the job well is better than doing 100 per cent poorly.

---

A new sales invoicing system was being developed. The basic system produced invoices from delivery notes, then passed the data to an open item sales ledger. One division of the company had a special product which was supplied in a different way to the rest of the company; this amounted to 2 per cent of total sales. This meant that the invoicing part of the system would have to be extended to cater for this special product. The time and cost of doing this was considerable. I examined the need and suggested that the work involved in adapting the system was not worthwhile, and that the invoices could be raised manually (as at present), and the invoice data input to the system for inclusion in the open item sales ledger. This approach kept the system simple and worked extremely well.

---

**Imposed limits**   I stated earlier that many limits are imposed to overcome poor design. Overcoming limits means improving the design. This might cause problems especially if trainers are not involved in the design process early enough. So if we can't, i.e. are not allowed to, improve design we have to study the limits and discover the exact reasons for them. This is done for two reasons. First, we need to know the reason so that we can explain it to learners. Second, by following this process, designers are often led to decide they want to change the system themselves. My simple rule for trainers is never accept that limits are necessary, always try to remove them.

**Operating speed**   The training programme that is produced should explain that users are in control of the system, which is just a tool for the more effective performance of job requirements. The way the system is designed should support this, but, as this is sometimes not the case, operators should be trained to concentrate on doing their job at a speed that suits them and the customer, and not to please the computer. Any system defaults, based on time, i.e. where the system reacts to some preprogrammed instruction such as to switch off, or move to the next transaction, should be removed from the system.

**User interface**   This subject is dealt with more fully in the next chapter, but for now I will stress how important it is for trainers to become knowledgeable about building interfaces that are designed for users, and not to meet the technical needs of the system.

# Overcoming practical barriers

The practical barriers of time, space and environment can be overcome by making clear recommendations on the best possible approach to the learning. Where possible, managers should be trained in the basic skills of supporting and helping people to learn. This will then make it possible for them to ensure that they give their staff the best possible conditions for learning.

**Time**     Learners should be given the chance to work at their own pace, and at a time when they choose to learn. For some this may be during the working day, for others it might mean when work is finished and they can concentrate on learning. Some people prefer to learn in the morning, others in the evening. There is no more important task than learning. Performance depends totally on how well people learn, and on how quickly they gain confidence. This does not mean that training has to be a lengthy process, but that whatever time people need is made available.

**Space**     When I refer to space I don't mean only physical space, but also psychological space. In devising learning environments trainers should be aware of both these aspects and attempt to make learners as comfortable as possible. One way to do this is to ask learners how they want to learn, and what they need to help them to learn.

**Environment**     One of the worst ways to accommodate learning, perhaps the most ineffective way possible, is to cram people into a classroom under the watchful, and often critical, gaze of the trainer. It doesn't seem to matter how the classroom is set out, in a U-shape or theatre style, the results are still awful. Yet this is the most common form of training throughout the world. It is particularly bad for learning to use technology, or when using technology to learn. So why do we do it?

I wish I knew the answer to this question. I no longer do it. I never operate in a classroom environment. The result is that learners learn better and faster, they have more confidence, and performance is considerably better much sooner than if I had attempted the classroom approach. Perhaps I should add that I was no slouch as a classroom trainer, and I seemed to get good results, but they were not even remotely close to the results I get since I abandoned the classroom approach.

Learning in the workplace is nothing new. It is where the majority of learning takes place. Such learning as happens at present may not be planned or supported, but it happens. If people have to perform they have to learn, and they will do so whether or not they are helped. It should not be assumed that managers know how to help their staff to learn, or that managers give the appropriate high priority to learning. Where necessary, models of the most appropriate environment should be built and efforts made to see that the recommendations and models are followed in practice.

**Easing psychological barriers**     There are five psychological barriers that have to be removed if trainers are going to develop training which is enjoyable and effective (see previous chapter). The first step in doing this is to recognize that the barriers exist and need to be removed. Removing the psychological barriers requires trainers to do three things:

- convert the unknown into the known;
- encourage people to concentrate on their strengths;
- develop positive motivation.

**Unknown → known**

The unknown becomes the known—this apparent contradiction is achieved by relating the new thing to be learned to something that the individual will already have experienced and dealt with successfully, e.g. driving a car, using a telephone, operating a washing machine. This approach softens the threat of the unknown and simplifies the concept of what has to be learned.

**Strengths**

Everybody has strengths, things that they accept they are good at. By bringing these out into the open and showing how they are important, an atmosphere of confidence is created. This can be done very successfully by asking the people involved to state what they are good at, and then getting them to consider how these attributes can be used in learning the new thing.

**Positive motivation**

It is possible to generate positive attitudes towards learning by the simple process of examining all the reasons why people should *not* bother to learn the specific task. What happens is that, by directing attention to the fact that it is okay not to want to do something, a strong positive feeling is generated to want to do it. This can be seen when children do exactly what they are told *not* to do.

Here is an example about the removal of psychological barriers.

---

A large UK company was introducing a new computer-based sales order processing system. The existing system worked via telephone sales staff who rang the customer and took the order, entering the details onto an order form. The new system required the orders to be entered directly into the system via a keyboard. The company wanted to train the existing staff to use the new system. All the psychological barriers were in evidence in the following ways:

- The staff feared the unknown new system. They understood and were happy using the existing system.
- All doubted their ability to work with the new system. Some of the staff had never even seen a computer terminal, let alone used one.
- Some of the older, highly skilled staff felt that the new system would mean a loss of status for them.
- None of the staff saw any convincing reason for the introduction of the new system.

These barriers were removed in the following way:

> The staff were asked whether they could operate a television, an adding machine and a typewriter. They all could. They were then shown the computer terminal which was a combination of all three. Next, they were asked how fast they thought they could input data via the keyboard. They decided that the speed depended on how quickly the customer gave them the order. They didn't need to learn to type, as most of the input was numerical.

The staff were asked what they were good at. The general answer was 'telephone selling'. The importance of telephone selling was emphasized and the technology was described as a new way of taking orders that would help them to sell more. As the staff were paid sales commission, this became an encouragement.

The final step was to offer the staff the choice of continuing to use the paper-based system, with other staff inputting the data into the system. They quickly recognized that this would not enable them to use the features of the new system that would help them to sell more, and so they chose to use the new system.

The net result was that the staff became very positively motivated to learn the new system, and did so very successfully.

---

Learning to do new things should be, and can be, fun. When the psychological barriers have been removed trainers can concentrate on making the training programme very enjoyable. To do this they have to know what people enjoy when they are learning. This will vary from person to person, but there are three key factors that make learning enjoyable and effective. These are:

• opportunity to choose what, and how, to learn;
• opportunity to experiment; and
• opportunity to self-monitor the learning.

When learning new technology, trainers can make use of the technology in an imaginative way. For example, the learners are introduced to the computer terminal and then allowed to decide how they want to go about learning. The emphasis should be placed on the ease and fun of using the technology to learn.

# Human barriers

One way to remove the human barriers to learning is to remove humans from the process. This is not the only way, but it can be very effective. Distance-learning materials, particularly computer-based programmes, remove the human barriers, but they also remove the advantage of human interaction. But is this necessary, and do such approaches really remove the human barriers? I believe the answer is *no*. All the human barriers can appear in a distance-learning programme because it has, of course, been produced by humans.

## Communication

If we have problems communicating when we speak, then it becomes even more difficult when we write. In *The Business of Training* I provide a set of writing standards which might help to overcome this problem, but perhaps the best approach for trainers is to make everything they try to communicate as simple as possible. In addition, trainers should make use of the widest array of stories, examples, models, etc. using analogy and metaphor as much as possible.

## Caring

A caring approach is perfectly possible to produce in the written word, and in the way that the training programme is designed. By giving learners many choices and options about the way they learn, the exercises they do, the amount of practice that is possible, we are in effect saying, 'I am trying to help you to learn in whichever way is best for you', which is a very caring approach.

By providing support and guidance within the training programme we are indicating that we care about how easy the learning is, and how effective it is. We can also introduce fun into the programme, which shows that we care about how interesting and enjoyable the learning is.

**Ego**  Ego, or the problems of excessive ego, can be overcome by thinking about the learners and the learning, and not about ourselves.

---

I remember producing an extremely simple paper-based (two-page) introduction to a complex computer system. My version replaced a 25-page booklet that had been written by the systems group. My draft was ridiculed. It was suggested that it wasn't impressive, and that it wasn't professional. It was very hard for me to persevere and produce this 'inadequate' and 'below-standard' product, but I did persevere. The result was that the learners, including top management, welcomed the new system with little if any apprehension.

---

In the above example, if I had let my ego get in the way I would have answered my critics with a so-called professional product, and failed to serve the needs of the learners.

**Personality**  I have no answers to offer about this barrier to learning. Perhaps all any of us can do is to be aware that who we are may need to be taken into account. We need to be responsive to other's reactions to us and to recognize that, as trainers, we do not, or should not be, judged by what we do, but by how good the learning outcomes are for the learners.

# Key points

• The way to overcome barriers to learning is to:
—remove them;
—go round them;
—reduce them; and/or
—go through them.

• To overcome technical barriers, analyse the system from the point of how the job is done, not how the system works.
• The training programme should advise users that they are in control of the system.
• Learners should be given the time and space they need.
• Do not assume that managers know how to help staff to learn.
• Do not assume that managers give the appropriate high priority to learning.
• Removing the psychological barriers means:
—converting the unknown into the known;

    —encouraging people to concentrate on their strengths;
    —developing positive motivation.
- Learning to do new things should be, and can be, fun.
- There are three key factors that make learning enjoyable and effective:
    —opportunity to chose what, and how, to learn;
    —opportunity to experiment; and
    —opportunity to self-monitor the learning.
- Overcoming human barriers means concentrating on learners and learning and not on ourselves.
- Training is helping people to learn, not a way of boosting our own egos.

---

**PRACTICAL APPLICATION**

Overcoming technology learning barriers is not difficult if these steps are followed:

- Ensure that the barriers are clearly defined and agreed.
- Design the training programme to give learners control of, and choice in, the way they steer themselves along the learning path.
- In the design stage of the development, ensure that learning problems are identified for every module and a specific solution chosen.
- Explain to learners where they might encounter a learning barrier and give them some help on how to overcome it.
- Try constantly to look at the learning from the viewpoint of the learner.
- Prepare a checklist of learning barriers and tick them off as you deal with them in the programme design.

# 6 The human/machine interface

The human/machine interface is the point at which users and the system come into contact. It usually involves a computer terminal with a screen and a keyboard. There could also be other devices for inputting data or signals to the computer. The interface consists of the way that the equipment is used, and the way that the system communicates with the user via the screen.

The user interface consists of two elements—the physical and the psychological. The physical interface deals with actions that the user takes, with particular reference to the use of the equipment. The psychological interface deals with the thinking and feeling that takes place during any interaction with the system.

There is a strong tendency for the design of systems to be highly patronizing. It seems that systems often treat users in the same way that parents treat children. The system makes demands, points out mistakes, sets rules, and generally 'talks down' to users. There is very little reasoning and explanation. Users are told what to do and how to do it.

## The physical interface

The equipment itself can put people off before they even start to learn to use it. There is, for example, a mistaken belief that people need to be able to type before they can use a keyboard. This is absolute nonsense. For many applications there is no need to enter alphabetical characters— most of the input is numerical. Of course, it helps if people can type, but it is not essential. The actions that users have to take with the equipment fall into four categories: control actions; inserting files; data input; and pressing keys.

## Control actions

These cover such things as switching on, logging on to the computer system, and starting work. This series of steps is often referred to as 'start up', or 'start of day'. Computer people refer to 'booting' the system, which simply means the process of switching on, setting up the system, and loading the program into the computer's memory. This process is now usually automatic. These control actions are usually very simple and easy to learn. What seems to put people off is the possibility of doing something wrong and damaging the system. They should be encouraged to 'mess about' with the system, and actually to try to do things wrong. In this way they will quickly learn that the system is quite capable of looking after itself.

The second set of control actions is associated with closing down, logging off, and switching off. Once again this process is usually very simple, but it needs to be learned, with particular emphasis on actions such as making security copies of files.

## Inserting files

This process means either putting disks into the machine, or retrieving files from memory. Though care needs to be exercised in handling disks, people should not be put off by dire warnings of how easy it is to damage them. A short training sequence on disk handling and file access should be quite sufficient.

It might help if the process of creating, storing and accessing files is explained by reference to paper-based files. Most computer users are familiar with filing so the computer approach can be made to appear very simple. It is also useful to show users that the computer will check with them before deleting files.

## Data input

Data input refers to typing in letters and numbers, usually in prescribed areas of the screen called 'fields'. New users should be introduced to the idea of the cursor, and the way that the cursor can be controlled and moved about the screen. This can be done playing a simple game, perhaps in the form of a crossword.

The principle of the shift key needs to be explained. My favourite approach to this learning process is to allow new users to play with the keyboard and see what happens. One of the most difficult things to learn are the functions of all the keys on the keyboard. This can be avoided by producing a simple system which demonstrates what happens when a key is pressed. Learners should be invited to discover the function of keys by actually pressing them and seeing what happens. This should include all function keys and combinations of keys.

There is another form of input which is best described as 'making a selection from some information presented on the screen'. This can be approached in four main ways. First is the moving of the cursor to the item to be selected, and then pressing 'enter'. Second is inputting a number or letter that corresponds to the item selected and pressing 'enter'. Third is using a 'mouse' to direct the pointer to the item and then 'clicking' the mouse. And finally is the 'touch screen' approach of actually pressing the item required on the screen. When asking users to input some data or to press a specified key to select something, the instruction should always be written in the sequence: description then action, e.g. 'To delete, press F2', not 'F2 = delete'. Unfortunately, most computer software does this the wrong way round. This is an example of what I call 'upside-down logic', which is one of the worst problems of the human/machine interface. Perhaps I should explain.

## Upside-down logic

When a system is being designed the designer is, quite rightly, concentrating on the functionality and performance of the system. This is at the back of the computer screen. When users use the computer they work from the other side, i.e. the front of the screen. This means that they see the logic of the designer from the other side or, as I say, upside down. You can visualize this by considering the way we address an envelope. Here is a sample address:

Dr Trevor J Bentley
Upper Steanbridge Mill
Slad
Stroud
Gloucestershire
England

When the address is written we start with the name because we want the item to go to that person at the address we list. When the envelope is in the postal system the address is read in the exact opposite way to which it is written.

In computer systems the program logic operates in this 'upside-down' way. For example, when systems check data for errors they check for specific things, e.g.

- the data should be there
- the data is numeric
- the data is four digits
- the data fits in the range 1000–3000

When using the system the user may receive any one of four messages explaining the reason the data has not passed the computer check, although some systems just report 'invalid data' and leave it for users to work out the problem. In fact, users only want to know what should be entered, i.e. a code that fits in the range 1000–3000, and where to find the code, in case they don't know.

**Pressing keys**

In many technology training programmes a simple device is used to allow users to move forward a screen at a time, equivalent to turning a page. To do this four different approaches are used. The most common is the instruction 'press any key', the second most used is 'return', then the 'enter' key, and finally the 'space bar'. There is very little consistency between different programmes.

When people are learning to use technology they should be encouraged to use the keys that they will use in their normal work. If the F4 key is used for 'next page', and F5 for 'previous page', then these are the keys that should be used during the training programme. If there are no pre-scribed keys then I would use 'space bar'. I believe that 'enter' should only be used when data is being input in some way, i.e. to tell the computer that there is something to do. I would never use the 'press any key' instruction—it is far too vague and often untrue.

# The psychological interface

When people use a computer system they react in a similar way to communicating with another person. They are, in fact, doing exactly this. The people they are communicating with are the system designers and programmers who have built the system. As with any human interface the language used, and the way it is used, affects the way that people feel and react. This is no less true of the human/machine interface.

There is also the very important aspect of *empathy*, which is the care and attention that designers have given to the interface, and the recognition that the system is going to be used by people who need help and support. In my experience this empathy is nearly always absent.

## Language

The standards for writing training material (see *The Business of Training*) have been produced to try to ensure that the human/machine interface is effective. If they are followed it is likely that users will react very well to the system. This is a very important topic, and so the whole of the next chapter has been devoted to the effective use of language.

## Screen design

There are four key elements of good screen design. The first is the layout; the second is the sequence of action; the third is the field descriptions; and the fourth concerns screen-based instructions (see Chapter 17 in *The Business of Training* for detailed screen design standards).

**Screen layout**  From the user's viewpoint it is better to have two widely spaced screens than one cramped screen. This is in conflict with the designer's aim to have fewer screens to process. The screen should be laid out going from left to right and top to bottom. The fields should start in the same vertical position, with descriptions to the left.

There should be a suitable title, or header line; the body of the screeen; and then a section for messages and instructions.

Colours should be used sparingly; observe some of the basic rules about colour combinations (see Chapter 17 in *The Business of Training*).

**Sequence of action**  Action, i.e. data entry, should start at the top left and proceed in a logical flow to the bottom right. All data for a similar purpose should be grouped in adjacent fields. When one field is completed the cursor should not automatically move to the start of the next field: users should be asked to press the 'Tab' key.

**Field descriptions**  All field descriptions should be English and should be full words that are meaningful. Abbreviations should not be used. Field descriptions should be self-explanatory.

**Screen instructions**  All screen instructions should be written in simple conversational English, without abbreviations. They should be active, e.g. 'to return to the previous screen, press F5'.

## Exercises

When learners do an exercise it is not a test, it is part of the learning process. Catching learners out by tricky questions or awkward requests is pointless. Exercises should always be written in the most helpful way possible. The aim should be for the learner to succeed. By being successful learners grow in confidence and are willing to tackle more difficult exercises.

Every exercise should give clear instructions about what is required, and where learners can find the information and examples to help them to complete the exercise successfully. There should be a clear indication of what represents successful performance, e.g. 'To complete this exercise successfully, you will need to create four new accounts and carry out all the transactions on these accounts so that the closing balances are as follows . . .'.

## Feedback

Feedback is information given by the system to users in response to some action taken by them. It should be helpful, encouraging, positive and progressive.

**Helpful feedback**   Messages such as 'well done' are not helpful. A helpful message is one that reiterates what has happened and makes a useful statement, e.g. *You have just calculated the interest payable over a two-year period as $4000. This is based on a rate of 10%. If the rate had been 12½% the interest would have been $5000.*

**Encouragement**   All learners need encouragement, but not in the form of the patronizing 'congratulations' type of comment. Encouraging feedback is information that supports the progress that learners are making, whether or not they get everything 'right'.

**Positive feedback**   Positive feedback gives success rates, not error rates. It does not state that something is wrong. It refers to what learners have done and says something like: *In the case of someone who has defaulted on a loan you would refuse a further loan, but in the case of someone who has a good repayment record you would probably give a further loan.*

**Progressive feedback**   This is feedback that moves learners forward. It will refer to what has happened and say something like: *After calculating the interest for a two-year loan you could calculate the interest over three years and compare them.*

The overall aim is to provide users with a good feeling when they are learning. Everything should be aimed at making it easy and comfortable for people to learn to use the technology. Far from being a 'soft option', this approach is a very powerful learning-centred technique that speeds up learning and considerably improves performance.

## Key points

- The human/machine interface is the point where users and the system interact.
- The interface consists of a physical element and a psychological element.
- The physical interface deals with actions that the user takes. The psychological interface deals with the thinking and feeling that occur during interaction with the system.

- The actions that users take are control actions, inserting files, data input and pressing keys.
- Instructions on the screen should be written with description followed by action, e.g. *To delete press F2*, not *F2 = delete*.
- Communicating with a computer is like communicating with another person.
- Good screen design pays attention to four things: the layout; the sequence of action; the field descriptions; and screen-based instructions.
- When learners do an exercise it is not a test, but part of the learning process.
- Feedback is information given to users in response to action taken by them. It should be helpful, encouraging, positive and progressive.

---

### PRACTICAL APPLICATION

- However poor the user interface is on the application for which training is being developed, ensure that the learning programme has an excellent interface.
- It is possible to overcome a poor user interface by showing learners what the problems are, and then providing help in overcoming them. If systems designers continue to design systems with bad user interfaces it is up to trainers to contradict them and to help users to overcome them.
- A good interface makes the system easy to use and easy to learn. It has four main features:
  —it puts the learner at ease;
  —it highlights, then overcomes, difficulties;
  —it plays down the importance and sophistication of the technology;
  —it helps and supports learners.
- Prepare a list of all the ways in which the training you are producing can simplify the understanding of the system.
- Think about how you would want to be helped and supported if you were learning the system.
- Test the interface you have designed by asking someone who knows nothing about the system to try to learn it from your training programme.

# 7 The effective use of language

This chapter seeks to add to the advice offered in Chapter 12 of *The Business of Training* by explaining some of the reasoning behind the way words are used when they are intended specifically for learners.

The first point to make is that the learners we are talking about are learning a wide variety of subjects. They are not generally learning the English language. Learning a language requires a very special use of words.

We use language to help us to communicate information, ideas, thoughts, feelings, etc. to other people. To do this we have to use words that our audience understand, i.e. words to which they can attach meaning. The language we use should be a practical help and not a barrier to learning. This is particularly the case in training for technology, especially when the training is computer-based. Frequently, in computer-based training, the screen has limited room and so the amount of text is limited. When this happens, the appropriate use of language becomes very important.

## Words as symbols

Words are used as convenient symbols. When I use the word 'tree' I have to make an assumption that my audience knows what a tree is. They might have different visual images of 'tree', but they will understand. If I add to this single word a descriptive word such as 'large', I have enhanced the visual image of the audience. If I now use these words in a sentence I create a picture of some event. *The large oak tree had fallen on the red sports car and crushed it.*

When we use words as symbols we hope that our audience will create the picture that we intend, or at least one very similar. In this way we can transfer thoughts, ideas and information to other people. However, if my audience do not have a store of word symbols as extensive as mine, I risk confusing them by giving them words for which they cannot find a relevant meaning. The human brain is very good at making a near fit, or guessing a meaning, but when you are writing for learning this can cause confusion.

See if you can produce a mental image for the following words:

| | | |
|---|---|---|
| combustion | conflagration | conine |
| galena | galbanum | gall |
| maund | maverick | gum |
| packet | pardalote | flight |

## Readability

Research has been carried out to establish what makes the English language easy to read and understand. The conclusion to this work is that the use of short words in short sentences makes text easy to read. Here is an extract from *The Complete Plain Words* by Sir Ernest Gowers.

A deduction of tax may be claimed in respect of any person whom the individual maintains at his own expense, and who is (i) a relative of his, or of his wife, and incapacitated by old age or infirmity from maintaining himself or herself, or (ii) his or his wife's widowed mother, whether incapacitated or not, or (iii) his daughter who is resident with him and upon whose services he is compelled to depend by reason of old age or infirmity.

This sentence, which is diffuse and difficult to follow, was later rewritten as follows:

If you maintain a relative of yourself or your wife who is unable to work because of ill health or old age, you can claim an allowance. You can claim this allowance if you maintain your own, or your wife's widowed mother, whether she is unable to work or not. If you maintain a daughter who lives with you because you or your wife are old or infirm, you can claim an allowance.

The idea of short words and short sentences has been developed into a way of calculating readability. This is called the Fogg Index. It is calculated by adding the average sentence length (in words) of a piece of writing to the percentage of words above two syllables used in the piece. The devisers of this index claim that a figure in the range 25 to 35 is highly readable, and that above 35 the text becomes increasingly difficult to understand.

I have calculated the Fogg Index for page 40 of this book and I arrived at the following index:

| | |
|---|---|
| average sentence length (in words) | 15 |
| % of words above two syllables | 15 |
| | 30 |

You can make your own judgement about the readability of page 40. My aim is always to write in the range 25 to 35. However, when I am writing computer-based information for training, help, or performance support systems, I try to aim for a Fogg Index of 20.

## Addressing the reader

There are three ways of addressing a reader, usually referred to as the first person, second person and third person. The first person style of writing uses the words 'I' and 'we' (e.g. *I* like to work with four approaches in mind). The second person uses the word 'you' (e.g. *You* will find this method will make *your* teaching more effective). And the third person refers to 'he', 'she' and 'they' (e.g. *Users* learn in the way *they* prefer).

When writing training material we want to develop a style which the reader feels comfortable with. This, I believe, should use mainly the second person. This book uses all three approaches, but is written primarily in the second person, and I hope that you have found it comfortable to read.

Too much use of the first person is like a conversation in which only one person is talking. It becomes a boring lecture. However, it is appropriate when describing personal experiences or when taking ownership for what you are saying (e.g. I could clarify my understanding by asking for a description of the mushroom).

Using the third person is remote and can distance the writer from the reader, but is useful for making comments that apply in general to large groups (e.g. Learners know that the guidance they receive . . .).

A good conversational style is very effective for learning. Learners feel involved and respond well to the flow of the text. When examples and exercises are used, learners feel that the training programme is friendly and helpful. However, even in the first and second person, it is possible to use words that put learners off.

## Hard/soft words

It is possible to create a piece of writing that is sharp and brittle, and makes the reader cringe. This is because the writer has used 'hard' words that give no option to the reader. Here is an example:

> *You will tell your manager when you make a mistake.*

The words *will, tell, when, make* and *mistake* are all hard in this context. They are imperative and commanding. 'Soft' words offer some degree of comfort, and do not alienate the reader. The sentence used above could be written as follows:

> *If you make an error you should inform your manager.*

This is much gentler and easier to accept. The word *make* is softened in this example by the word *if*.

## Approach

It is always preferable to indicate what people should do rather than what they should not do, and this is particularly important when writing training materials. Here are some examples of negative approaches:

> *You must not shout at customers.*
> *Do not accept credit cards as proof of identity.*

And here are the positive versions:

> *Customers react badly if you shout at them.*
> *Customers must offer some proof of identity other than credit cards.*

I have been told that the positive approach used above is less direct and harder to learn. I don't accept this view. I strongly believe that the positive approach is always the best one for learning.

## Grammar

Ernest Gowers wrote this about grammar in his famous book *The Complete Plain Words*:

> I have ample evidence . . . that too much importance is attached to the grammarians' fetishes and too little to choosing the right words.

Of course, without any grammar there would probably be chaos, and so we need to observe some basic standards that will give form and meaning to our words without creating a rigid and complex structure.

## Arrangement of words

When we put words into a sentence we arrange them to give the desired meaning. It is important to consider the meaning a *reader* might construe from our words, rather than to be content with the meaning we *think* we have conveyed. Now this is never easy, for how can a writer also be a reader? One way is to ask someone else to explain the meaning, another is to try to read different meanings into what we have written.

Here is an example of what can happen if we don't pay attention to word arrangement.

> *After crying she smiled with her large red eyes.*

Or we could say:

> *She smiled with her large eyes, red from crying.*

Or:

> *Her large eyes were red from crying when she smiled.*

Or:

> *After crying her large eyes were red, and she smiled.*

All these sentences use the same words, but by arranging them differently I am able to convey different meanings. Some are funny, some sad, and the last one implies that she was smiling because her eyes were red.

When producing training material, particularly for technology-based training, it is important to check carefully that the meaning is exactly what we want it to be. We can do this by deciding what we want to say before we write it, and then try several ways of saying it.

## Idiom

Idiom refers to expressions that are generally accepted, but which are difficult to explain grammatically—e.g. *fill in the form, come across with, home town*. We know what these phrases mean, not because the words make sense in themselves, but because we have learned the meaning from common usage. Idiomatic phrases are usually impossible to translate directly into another language.

Idiomatic expressions help to create a smooth and easily understood way of writing, and so they are acceptable in the writing of training materials.

Grammar is, therefore, a way of controlling the way we write so that the reader is helped to get the meaning that we intend. We can use grammar in a flexible way as long as the meaning comes through sharp and clear.

## Key points

- Language is used to communicate information, ideas, thoughts, feelings, etc. to others.
- Language should be a practical help and not a barrier to learning.
- Words are used as convenient symbols so that our audience will create the picture we intend.
- The use of short words in short sentences makes text easy to read.
- Calculating readability can be done using the Fogg Index.
- Training material needs a style the reader feels comfortable with.
- Use of the second person style makes readers feel comfortable.
- Too much use of the first person is like a one-way conversation.
- Using the third person is remote and can distance the writer from the reader.
- Sharp and brittle writing, using 'hard' words, puts the reader off.
- It is preferable to indicate what people should do rather than what they should not do.

---

### PRACTICAL APPLICATION

- **Check that the language you are using is made up of simple, well-known words that have a precise meaning.**
- **Calculate the Fogg Index for your written material.**
- **Edit your material, removing long or obscure words.**
- **Reduce the length of every sentence.**
- **Reduce every paragraph by one sentence.**
- **Avoid using the words *no, not, can't, won't, don't*; replace them with positive words.**
- **Ask a friend to read your writing and to be *very* critical in a constructive way.**

---

# 8 Understanding and communication: the role of analysis

When we learn, although we are probably unaware of it, we go through a process which is a form of analysis. This process receives information about our environment and leads towards full understanding.

When we receive information from our senses we automatically try to match this with our existing memories and experience. This matching process is often automatic but, whether or not we are aware of it, it takes place. The next step is to interpret the meaning of the information we have received. Sometimes we clarify what we think the information means, and sometimes we don't. We might not have time, because we need to act immediately to avoid an accident or to escape from danger. When we do have time, we usually like to test our understanding and, if possible, to get some feedback. The feedback may either consolidate our understanding or send us back to the interpretation stage.

I have just come in from a walk during which I collected about twenty species of fungi. From previous experience, I have selected two sorts for the frying pan; the rest, some no doubt very tasty, have been thrown in the bin. I have a pretty good idea that one of the species I have thrown away is a particularly edible mushroom but, unfortunately, my current level of knowledge is insufficient for me to take the risk of receiving damaging and painful feedback if I should happen to be wrong. This is one occasion when I am not prepared to learn from experience.

The process we follow when learning can be divided into six steps:

- sensory input
- message interpretation
- clarification
- testing understanding
- receiving feedback
- consolidating understanding

## Sensory input

I have already stated that learners use all their senses when learning, and that good training tries to feed as many of the senses as possible. When input is received it is processed to establish whether it is:

- familar and known (understood);
- familiar and unknown; or
- unfamiliar.

**Familiar and known**   This category of information contains concepts of which we have had sufficient previous knowledge and experience, so that we can say with confidence, as I have just done, that I know this is an edible mushroom.

**Familiar and unknown**   Perhaps this is the most difficult category because I am tempted to allow the familiarity of what I see or hear to confuse me into believing I know what it is. In the case of mushrooms this could be very dangerous, even though I know that most species are safe. I do, therefore, need more information from a reliable source to enable me to learn enough to take the next step to consolidate my understanding, i.e. by eating the said mushrooms.

**Unfamiliar**   This is clear-cut. The information is unfamiliar to me, so I need more information before I do anything, or learn anything.

If the input falls into the first category then the process can continue and the message which contains the input can be interpreted. If the input falls into the second or third category, and if additional help isn't given, learners become unable to process the message further. This is when learners need to ask questions to help them to sort out the input.

## Message interpretation

As the message is received, provided the input is familiar and known, learners can proceed to interpret its meaning. This interpretation process involves checking the information with a known store of images, held in the brain, for which meanings already exist, or of discovering the meaning of the images created by the message. This may lead to more questions, or a search in external stores for help. A dictionary is an obvious source of information for helping us to interpret messages.

In the design of a training programme, particularly one that uses the computer, trainers should be aware of the learners' need to explore the meaning of the message they are receiving. Facilities can be provided for learners to access several levels of additional information, from simple 'Help' messages to extensive libraries of information and examples.

This process of interpretation and discovery is one of the most exciting aspects of learning. Making sense of what we already know, or discovering new things, stimulates and excites most people.

## Clarification

Once we think we have interpreted (understood) the message correctly we need to seek clarification. This may be done in the form of a question such as 'Do you mean that . . . ?' or it may be done by checking the information with someone else: 'I think this means that . . .'.

Many learners are hesitant to clarify what they think they understand for fear of looking silly. The clarification process is very important and training programmes should constantly provide an opportunity for learners to clarify their understanding. If this is not done it is possible for learners to complete a programme with misunderstandings and confusion.

Ways to provide opportunities for clarification include giving the message from several different viewpoints, or using different analogies and metaphors so that learners can see that what they understood the first time is the same from a different aspect.

In the case of my learning about mushrooms, I could clarify my understanding by asking for a description of the mushroom, by looking at a picture of the mushroom in its growing state, by looking at a picture in the picked state, both from above and below. Then I could be asked to describe what it looks like when I cut it open, and I could compare my description either with a picture or text.

Giving learners exercises to do is a much better way of clarifying understanding than presenting them with a series of simple questions. Questions may help me to 'think I know', whereas exercises make sure I *understand* by asking me to use the information I 'think I know'. These kinds of exercises are designed to help people to learn, not given as tests, which is a very important distinction. During learning exercises learners should be able to call on all the sources of information that were available to them while learning.

## Testing understanding

There is nothing quite as exciting as testing something new. If we think we understand how to do something, actually doing it is an excellent test of whether our understanding is correct. It is thought by many trainers and educationalists that understanding can be tested by asking questions. By their very nature, questions elicit knowledge, which is not the same as understanding. Questions used during learning may help people to check what they know, but questions are not appropriate for testing understanding.

---

I was asked to review a programme that was used to train managers to carry out financial analysis of small businesses. The programme included a large section (about 30 per cent of the total) that dealt with ratio analysis. All the relevant ratios, and some not so relevant, were defined and the formulas for their calculation. An example was also given, and the trainer explained the use of each ratio. Subsequent to this training, the managers were given a set of accounts and asked to calculate the ratios and comment.

This seems like a fair test of understanding, but in fact it is only a test of memory; though most managers did the test very well few of them understood what they were doing. To assess this, I gave a group of managers who had completed the training a set of accounts and asked if they would grant the company a £250 000 loan and, if so, under what conditions. The outcomes varied greatly and indicated that the learners didn't understand what they had 'learned'.

I suggested that the training be changed, so that it start with an exercise without giving any direction or information. The learners would have to ask for what they needed to know. Each request for information would be answered by showing them how to extract it from the accounts, calculating ratios where necessary. In this way the learners could discover what they needed to know and how to get it. By doing this in small groups managers were able to help each other and share what they learned. This revised programme was extremely successful in generating understanding.

---

Understanding is tested by asking learners to apply their knowledge to the solution of some problem. The problem could be set as a mental or physical problem; it depends upon the learning environment. Problem-solving exercises which call on learners to apply what they have learned are by far the best way of testing understanding. Such testing is done, or at least it should be done, for the benefit of learners and not for the benefit of trainers. There is nothing worse or, alas, more common than tests designed to 'weed out' those who don't know. These are never for the benefit of the learner. If we want to discover the level of understanding of learners, then we need to present them with problems to solve, and to do so in the way that they would normally use to solve them in the real world, i.e. with access to all the supporting information they need. Examinations constrained by limited access to information, within limited time frames, are nothing more than a test of memory.

## Feedback

Having tested understanding via an appropriate exercise, we need to know how we have performed. It is imperative that we receive encouraging, informative and supportive feedback. Comments like 'well done', 'congratulations', 'oh dear', and so on are completely useless.

Effective feedback refers to the problem, indicates what we have done, and interprets our action. This should always be done from the point of view of success, i.e. it should comment on how successful we have been. If the attempt was not very successful, the feedback should give reasons why and offer a solution for us to look at if we want to. If we have been successful, the feedback should state why, and still offer a solution for comparison (see page 44 for more comments on feedback as part of the human/machine interface).

The purpose of feedback is threefold:

• to reinforce learning;
• to assess learning progress; and
• to encourage learning.

**Reinforcing learning**   When people learn, their initial response to what they learn is normally tentative. They display a form of diffidence to using their new learning. It is important that their learning is reinforced by simple exercises in which it is almost impossible for them not to succeed. This does not mean that these exercises are patronizing, but that they enable learners to display their new talents. Gradually, confidence grows and the feedback reinforces this with comments and more difficult exercises.

**Assessing learning progress**   One of the most common unspoken questions of learners is 'How well am I doing?' Not only should trainers provide feedback about the level of performance, but learners should be able to determine this for themselves against specific performance targets. In other words, learners should be able to assess their own learning progress as they proceed through the training programme.

One way to enable learning progress to be assessed is to set up a series of targets, so that at certain points in the learning process learners can go to a particular exercise and see how well they can do. This might even be the final exercise that is intended to assess the whole of the learning for that programme. The training programme should be able to record how well they do each time they attempt the exercise and thus show how they are improving.

**Encouraging learning**   Sometimes, even with the best programmes, learning can flag. When this happens it is important that the feedback that learners receive encourages them to continue. This might mean finishing at a logical point to which they can return with relative ease. Programmes should be structured in a way that facilitates this on-and-off approach. Feedback should never put learners off by telling them they are wrong, or that they are not doing too well, or making them feel inadequate. We do not encourage learning by making it seem difficult, or by highlighting the learner's problems. This can only lead to discouragement, which is the exact opposite of what we want.

# Consolidation

The final step in the process is to consolidate our understanding of what we have learned. Repeated successful performance in a variety of different situations is perhaps the best way to consolidate understanding.

This process can be watched as children learn to ride a bike. Once they have managed the first wobbly solo performance they continue to ride until their understanding of balance is firmly built into their mental and physical awareness.

On a recent skiing course I finally grasped the principle of carving a parallel turn. The instructor told me to keep practising and to *sense* what was happening. 'Do it until it is second nature,' he shouted as I skied off.

In computer-based training programmes, particularly those concerned with learning new systems, it is important to provide the opportunity for learners to practise what they have learned by providing a comprehensive set of practice exercises. These are different from learning exercises. Practice exercises should provide a range of tasks, often repetitive, which give learners the chance to practise what they have learned. During these exercises they should have available only the kind of help that will be available when they are 'on the job'. If they get stuck then they will have to return to one of the learning modules to continue, so the programme structure should allow this. There is an old saying that 'Practice makes perfect'. Training can never take learners beyond the point of having enough confidence to try to perform. It is the continuing trying which eventually leads to the desired performance levels.

## Key points

- When we learn we go through a six-step process:
  —sensory input
  —message interpretation
  —clarification
  —testing understanding
  —receiving feedback
  —consolidating understanding
- When input is received it is processed to establish whether it is:
  —familiar and known (understood)
  —familiar and unknown; or
  —unfamiliar.
- When new information is received which is unknown or unfamiliar, learners are unable to process the message further.
- Interpretation involves checking the new information with a known store of images, or of discovering the meaning for the new images.
- Training programmes should constantly provide an opportunity for learners to clarify their understanding.
- Understanding is tested by asking learners to apply their knowledge to the solution of some problem.
- Effective feedback refers to the problem, indicates what learners have done, and interprets their action.
- The purpose of feedback is threefold:
  —to reinforce learning;
  —to assess learning progress; and
  —to encourage learning.
- Repeated successful performance in a variety of different situations is perhaps the best way to consolidate understanding.

---

### PRACTICAL APPLICATION

- **Ensure that every training module feeds the six steps in the learning process.**
- **Use several analogies/metaphors for every key point you make in the programme.**
- **Provide frequent opportunities for clarification. Use a built-in dictionary, or a source of context-sensitive information.**
- **Produce lots of exercises so that learners have a wide choice.**
- **Write clear, effective feedback. It is part of the learning process, not just a brief response.**
- **Provide plenty of opportunity for practice.**

# 9 Continuous learning

Learning which takes place in a vacuum, in an artificial environment, and which cannot be continuously practised, soon fades. The aim should be to provide learners with sufficient assistance for the move into the real environment in which they will apply their learning.

I believe there are two stages of learning: initial learning and continuous learning. In technology training it is perfectly feasible to build both stages into the system. For other forms of learning this is more difficult, as the real environment, although it functions as a learning space, does so by default rather than intention.

The two stages of learning can be defined as follows:

**1  Initial learning**   This stage is concerned with giving learners the basic knowledge and skills they need to have the confidence to do something, albeit to a low level of performance. This stage, which we usually call training, rarely takes people up to the competence level, although there are some obvious exceptions to this, such as airline pilots.

**2  Continuous learning**   This is the stage that people are in when they are not doing initial learning; i.e. people are always learning even if they are unaware of the fact that they are learning. This stage is rarely referred to as training. We can build very effective continuous learning environments by acknowledging that as people work, play, etc. they are also learning.

## The learning curve

The learning curve is a simple and well-known approach for depicting the stages of learning that learners go through when moving towards becoming competent, and then highly skilled. I show it in Fig. 9.1 to give some indication of the emphasis that is placed on the two main stages of learning.

The curve depicted will, of course, change in steepness and length depending on the learners, the topic and the training approach used. However, the curve shown is representative of what is a likely trend in all forms of learning.

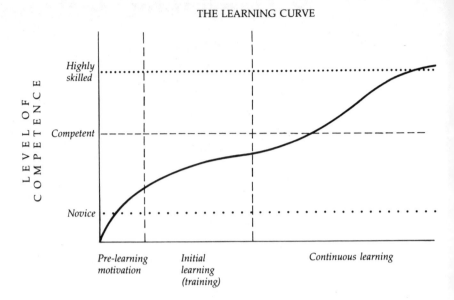

**Figure 9.1** *The learning curve*

# Pre-learning motivation

The two primary stages of learning are usually preceded by a decision phase where potential learners decide that for some reason they are ready to learn something. The reasons can be quite varied, and can be both positive and negative, but for whatever reason learners will have made the decision to learn.

It is important during the analysis and design phase of the training programme to determine what the main reasons are for people wanting to learn the particular topic. This will help when putting together the key learning needs, and when writing the opening module of the programme.

The opening module of the programme should contain enough information about the training programme, the guidance system, the choice of learning, the fun, and the chance to explore, to excite and motivate learners. It is very dangerous to assume that all learners are approaching the learning with a high level of positive motivation. This is particularly true of technology training.

# Initial learning

This is the stage when learners are first given the opportunity to learn the subject. This is the stage we call training and should provide learners with the opportunity to choose how to go about their learning, taking the modules in any sequence. The exercises should provide enough scope to consolidate understanding fully before learners move into the real environment where the continuous learning stage starts.

The main elements of the initial learning stage are:

- guidance
- experimentation
- exploration
- play

- information
- exercises
- practice
- feedback

**Guidance** in initial learning relates to guiding learners through the learning process. This means constantly giving maps and signposts so that learners know where they are, and how to get to where they want to be. This is particularly true when using technology as a learning medium because it is so easy to get lost in the computer's complexity.

**Experimentation** is one of the main ways for people to learn. By experimenting, people discover what happens when they do something. This is a powerful and direct way to learn. However, not everyone likes to learn this way so experimentation should be provided as an option. In fact, all modules should be options.

**Exploration**   When presented with new things, some people like to explore what they see before them. They want to have a look round before they do anything. This might be just to familiarize themselves with the new. During this exploration it is quite possible that they will learn things about the training. I frequently provide learners with an opening module which encourages them to explore the programme.

**Play**   I despair that I will ever find the answer to why adults won't admit that they love playing. We all love playing. As children we learn most of what we know through playing, yet as adults play is seen as a form of relaxation, i.e. something which has no useful outcome apart from pleasure. When we do play as adults we often spoil it by taking it seriously. Professional sport is a prime example of this. In training, play can be built in as an enjoyable and effective way of learning.

**Information**   During initial learning learners will want information to answer questions and to give meaning to what they are doing. I believe that information should be made available on an 'as needed' basis, rather than expecting learners to gather large amounts of facts and figures before they do something. There is nothing worse than a training programme that presents page after page of text, especially if it is revealed one sentence at a time by pressing the space bar. Give information in blocks on request.

**Exercises**   I have already said quite a bit about exercises, so here I will limit myself to three points. Exercises should be many, and varied, and of differing complexity. They should be available whenever learners want to have a go. They should support and encourage learners while they are doing them.

**Practice**   Protected and supported practice is a vital ingredient of initial learning. There just cannot be too much.

**Feedback**   Enough was said about this in the previous chapter, at least for the moment.

# Continuous learning

The real environment should be geared up for the continuous learning and development of performance. With technology training this can be done by building systems that are fully equipped to support continuous learning. (Chapter 13 provides an overview of how this can be achieved.)

The seven segments of the continuous learning stage are a little different from the initial learning stage. They are:

- guidance
- support
- information
- experience
- play
- exercises
- feedback

**Guidance**   This segment guides new users to the sources of information and/or learning that they are looking for. It can be the first module of a special training system linked to the operating system, or a fully embedded part of the system. It will offer users the equivalent of a street map of the support available from the system.

**Support** will come in all shapes and sizes, from simple tables of data to extensive calculation and advice systems. Ideally, users should be able to ask the system questions and receive context-sensitive replies. Support will probably include an error guidance and correction resource.

**Information** can be provided in all kinds of ways, from simple 'Help' to extensive on-line procedures and/or training guides. Users could be linked into a wide range of databases (see Chapter 13).

**Experience**   As the experience of users increases, so their needs will change. It is perfectly feasible to provide information and support for different levels of experience. This might be at three levels for, say, novice, competent and expert. Certainly, increasing experience and improving performance should be monitored and acknowledged.

**Play**   The application system should be robust enough to allow users to experiment and play with different transactions and tasks to 'see what happens'. This is an important learning process.

**Exercises**   Users should always have access to a range of exercises to try things out and to further the consolidation of their understanding.

**Feedback**   When the system responds to users it should do so in a way that reinforces learning and encourages and supports users. This applies to all feedback from error messages to requests for information.

The creation of a continuous learning environment for technology training goes way beyond the building of training programmes; it goes to the very heart of the analysis and design of good systems. It is no longer sufficient for training to overcome the barriers to technology learning. Systems have to be designed and built from the start to supply continuous support for users.

**Key points**
- Learning which cannot be continuously practised soon fades.
- There are two stages of learning: initial and continuous.
- The opening module of the programme should excite and motivate learners.
- The initial learning stage should provide choice in how to learn.
- The real environment should be geared up for the continuous learning and development of performance.
- The guidance segment points new users to the sources of information and/or learning that they are looking for.
- Support should be provided in many different ways.
- The application system should allow users to experiment and play.
- The creation of a continuous learning environment goes to the very heart of the analysis and design of good systems.

---

**PRACTICAL APPLICATION**

- The building of continuous training means establishing the need for user support, and then ensuring the technology makes it possible for users to get this support.
- Training programmes should be built so that they are available as a form of support.
- We never stop learning, so the environment we work in should enable us to continue to learn and grow. Make sure that users have easy access to the support they need via the system.
- If continuous learning support cannot be embedded, see if it can be built concurrently (see Chapter 13 for further information on this point).

# PART THREE

# The power of technology

# Introduction

This section of the book is concerned with the effective use of technology, particularly when it is being used to help people to learn to use technology.

Using technology to help people to use technology seems an obvious thing to do, and yet much of technology is still unfamiliar and indecipherable to the new user. Some of the most widely used and, hence, 'best-selling' software is of this kind, and yet people persist in struggling to learn to use it. The aids that are now provided, if the software producers are really on the ball, seem to include a computer-based tutorial, a comprehensive manual and a quick tips card. Unfortunately, the tutorials are very poor, the manuals are almost unreadable, and the quick tips card only works when you know how to use the system.

Why is this happening, and what can we do to improve the situation by using the power of the computer? This is what this section sets out to answer.

*Chapter 10    The strengths and weaknesses of technology*

This chapter looks at what the computer is good at, and what it is poor at. I then set out to show how to harness the strengths and overcome the weaknesses. Of course, I look at the strengths and weaknesses from the user's, and hence the learner's, point of view. That is why this chapter has a lot to offer systems designers who want to produce easy-to-use and easy-to-learn systems.

*Chapter 11    The power of technology training*

One of the difficulties that many trainers express is their lack of understanding of how the computer can be used to produce really effective training. One young woman recounted her experience in trying to persuade a systems designer to change a particular feature of the system. The designer acknowledged that what she was suggesting would be desirable, but that the work involved in changing the system would be enormous and time was at a premium. In this chapter I provide a basic guide to helping trainers get the best from systems designers, and hence the systems.

*Chapter 12    Simulations*

Simulations are an excellent way of providing learners with the opportunity to experience the situation they are learning about without placing them into the real environment. This is essential if the environment is threatening or hazardous. A simulation can be described as an imitation of reality. In training the closer we can get to reality, the sooner learners will move along the learning curve.

*Chapter 13    Performance support systems*

In my previous book in this series, *The Business of Training*, Chapter 19, written by Gloria Geary, defines an electronic performance support system (EPSS). I do not intend to repeat this material here. Instead I will concentrate on how to make EPSS happen, and on describing and explaining some of the problems and pitfalls in following the EPSS approach.

*Chapter 14    Making technology training successful*

This is the crunch chapter. In the past ten years I have met three types of trainers: those who will having nothing to do with computers (usually management development and personal growth people); those who have tried to use computers for training and have either failed or given up in disgust; and those who have tried, have to some extent succeeded and are persevering.

In this the final chapter I provide what I believe are the golden keys to open the door to success in harnessing technology for training.

The aim of this part of the book is to provide trainers with a guide to using technology successfully. Further study and learning will be necessary for beginners, but I intend that the information I provide will form a foundation that will ensure the development of improved technology-based training.

# 10 Using technology to overcome technology limitations

When technology is used to help people to learn to use technology, it is important for the training designers to understand the strengths and weaknesses of the technology. Once you can grasp what the technology is good at, it is possible to use this to overcome those things that the technology is poor at.

The first part of the chapter looks at those things that the computer is good at, and this is used as a basis for considering the limitations and how they can be overcome.

## Technology strengths

From a training point of view technology is very good at four things:

- providing information
- demonstrating
- providing exercises
- giving feedback

### Information

Computers have always been good at receiving, manipulating, storing, accessing and presenting information, hence the idea of the 'information revolution'. From a training point of view this means three things. First, learners can get the information they need when they need it; second, they don't have to exercise their brains remembering things that can be remembered by the computer; and, third, they have a lot less to learn to become competent users.

### Demonstration

The technology available, as I write, can provide lifelike simulations and demonstrations using text, graphics, audio and visual media, and all in full colour. The ability to demonstrate, especially if learners are learning to use the system, is a very powerful learning aid because a great deal of the learning we do is done via observation and copying.

### Exercises

I am aware of how often I have referred to exercises as I have been writing this book. I make no apology for this because I believe that the exercise is a vital but widely underutilized tool for learning. If I were designing a learning programme, approximately 60 per cent would be devoted to exercises and practice. This is one of the reasons I enjoy using technology for training. The computer is excellent at presenting exercises and at recording performance for subsequent feedback.

**Feedback**     The computer has a great capacity for feedback. It can provide information, guidance, etc., either when requested or when it decides to (according to some preprogrammed rules). The computer has the capacity to watch everything that the learner is doing and, if desirable, to keep a record. With this capacity, both in memory size and speed, it is possible to provide extremely supportive feedback.

Of course, all these strengths will only be available if careful attention is paid to the needs of users, and if the computer programs are written in the appropriate way. To do this it is necessary for systems designers to remember the impact of 'upside-down logic' and to produce systems that counteract it.

# Technology limitations

Technology is poor at:

- responding to learners' questions;
- deviating from the programmed approach;
- interacting intelligently;
- providing choice; and
- allowing exploration and experimentation.

Technology can only function in the way that it has been programmed to function. Even expert systems are limited within the framework of the rules. These rules can be added to, but at any one time there are limits. This means that we have to work within the limits and explore just how far we can stretch them. When helping people to learn an existing application system our first limit is the system itself. If we assume that we can't change the system then we have to work around the limits imposed by the designers. It is preferable, of course, if we can influence the design to remove limits, but we will examine the worst scenario.

**Responding to**     When people learn they frequently want to ask questions to help them
**questions**     to interpret the messages they are receiving. The vast majority of such questions can be predicted if the training analysis has been thorough. It then becomes possible to prepare a complete list of answers to questions that might be asked. Using technology, it is possible to store large amounts of such information. The problem is to provide a simple way for learners to access the answers. Using technology, we can overcome this by looking at three levels of questions: general explanations, specific questions, and word meanings.

Alternative, more detailed, or simplified explanations of the message that learners are asking about can be given. This can be triggered by giving learners an option such as 'If you understand, press the space bar; if you want clarification, press F6'.

Specific questions are dealt with by providing a space for learners to type in their questions. This will be of a limited size, and some basic writing rules might need to be established. The technology will then search its extensive set of questions and provide the appropriate answers. If, in practice, learners type in questions that aren't in the library, they can be stored and learners can be referred to their supervisor. At a later stage the stored questions are printed out, answers are written and the database extended with both questions and answers. Experience indicates that, with good training analysis, 75 per cent of questions can be covered and then within a short period of use the level can rise to 95 per cent.

The meaning of words and phrases can be provided by installing a dictionary that functions on highlighted words. Learners place the cursor on the word and select the designated dictionary key. The meaning is then displayed.

**Deviating from programmed approach**

This problem can be overcome by ensuring that the training programme is a 'free-format' approach, i.e. that it does not have a specified sequence. By providing a map of the programme, learners are able to navigate around the programme in any way that they want.

Nothing is more frustrating for learners than having to follow an approach devised by someone else who might have a preference for an 'informed' learning style when learners might want to use an 'exploratory' learning style. It is also frustrating when learners want to change their minds, but can't until they have waded through the current module.

**Interacting intelligently**

Technology developments are making it increasingly feasible for systems to interpret what users are trying to do and respond to them more intelligently. However, such facilities might not be available. The way for the trainers to overcome this, using the technology, is to ensure that their own intelligent response to learners is built into the training programme.

This is achieved by ensuring that the analysis and design stages of the training programme development are thorough and detailed. With this in-depth knowledge of the system, training designers can anticipate the interaction of learners and react accordingly. It should be your intelligence which is reflected in the reaction of the programme and not the system designer's.

Naturally, not every interaction of learners can be anticipated; when an unexpected interaction occurs, the programme has to respond with an answer such as: 'I am afraid I don't know the answer to what you have done, but please contact me on 223-6678 and I will try to sort it out'.

**Providing choice**

Technology can provide a certain degree of choice, such as menus and command codes. These are very basic and we need to apply our minds to how we can provide much more choice than this. I would like to explore four ways that choice can be expanded for learners. These are:

- open questions
- random selection
- descriptive menus
- learning maps

**Open questions**   This works by presenting learners with a screen on which they type the answer to an open question such as: 'What would you like to do now?' The programme then searches its extensive store of possibilities and presents learners with what they want. If what they have requested is not in store, the programme responds with a suggestion that user's talk to their supervisor or ring 223-6678.

This approach is often scoffed at by systems designers, but it is perfectly feasible. The important thing to ensure is that, when a request can't be met, the learner is given an intelligent response and not a pointless comment such as 'request unavailable'.

**Random selection**   This is my favourite, and is great fun. Learners are presented with a screen containing a display of pictures or words that do *not* depict or relate to what learners will get if they select that particular symbol. The outcome is a surprise. The computer can apply an algorithm which constantly changes the relationship between the symbols and the learning module presented. This is, of course, an alternative for learners who want some fun. If learners know what they want, they should be able to go straight to it.

**Descriptive menus**   Have you noticed how systems designers try to reduce menus to one-word lists? I can understand this for regular, skilled users, but for learners we need more information. This can be done using pictures or sentences which depict or describe what learners will get if they make that selection.

Such menus could also be valuable for regular users who sometimes forget infrequently used choices. Descriptive menus are so easy to produce that it seems criminal they're not widely used, especially in training programmes.

**Learning maps**   I have already described the idea of providing a map for learners to examine, and then to choose the path they want to follow. Using graphics and touch-sensitive screens, this could become a really 'fun' way of choosing what you want to do.

The learning map could be a module in itself and be built like a short computer game. Learners could try different paths and see where they might be led. Once they have decided they could input their chosen route and the training programme would guide them along it.

**Exploration/ experimentation**   Many learners prefer to learn by exploring and experimenting with the subject they are learning. Training programmes should be built to make this possible by allowing learners to choose to learn from descriptive exercises and demonstrations. When they do something wrong, the programme should respond with a suitable corrective suggestion from which they can learn. Technology is very good at providing demonstrations and exercises. This strength has to be expanded by providing more learner interaction during both demonstrations and exercises, and by providing free-format exercises that allow learners to play with the target system.

## Key points

- Designers in technology training need to understand the strengths and weaknesses of the technology.
- Technology only functions according to its programming.
- Computer technology has four strengths:
  —providing information
  —demonstrating
  —providing exercises
  —giving feedback
- Computer technology has five weaknesses:
  —responding to learners' questions
  —deviating from the programmed approach
  —interacting intelligently
  —providing choice
  —allowing exploration and experimentation
- With intelligent training analysis, 75 per cent of learners' questions can be covered, and within a short period of use the level can rise to 95 per cent.
- The meaning of words and phrases can be provided by installing a dictionary.
- The programmed approach can be deviated from by using free-format approach (no specified sequence).
- Intelligent interaction is created by building the training designer's own intelligent response to learners into the training programme.
- Choice can be expanded for learners in four ways:
  —open questions
  —random selection
  —descriptive menus
  —learning maps
- Always give the learner an intelligent response, not a pointless comment such as 'request unavailable'.
- Give more learner interaction during demonstrations and exercises, and provide free-format exercises that let learners play with the target system.

---

### PRACTICAL APPLICATION

- All the points raised in this chapter require application through applying imagination and common sense to the use of the training programme software.
- Avoid rigidity by not building a single sequence into the training.
- People learn their own way, not your way.
- Study the technology you are using to create the training programme, so that you know how to expand its apparent limitations.
- There is always a way of solving a problem—it is finding it that can sometimes be difficult.

# 11 The power of technology training

Using technology as a means of training, particularly for training in the use of technology, is a very powerful learning medium. Learners find that they learn easily and quickly. There are six main reasons for this:

- The learning enviornment is close to reality.
- Learners work at their own pace.
- Learners learn in the way they want to.
- They are supported during learning.
- Programmes are interesting and entertaining.
- There is plenty of variety and flexibility.

Of course, these reasons apply to good technology-based training that has been designed and built with learners in mind. This means that trainers have to get the system they want from the system designers. This is possible if five steps are taken:

- Accept that building good functional systems is difficult.
- Help systems designers counteract 'upside-down logic'.
- Persuade systems designers to change the system.
- Avoid becoming enchanted by technology.
- Press hard for simple, easy-to-use systems.

## Good technology training

The production of good technology-based training, especially when it is used to learn about technology, depends to a large extent on the quality of the user interface that is available. By looking first at what contributes to good technology training, we can understand more clearly the importance of getting the system we want from the designers.

### Learning environment is close to reality

People learn best in a real environment where they have to face life as it really is. The closer the learning environment can be to this real-life environment, the better. In technology training where learners are learning about the technology, we can make the training environment very real. In fact, in embedded CBT learners are actually learning from the live system.

Learners see the system they are learning as it actually is, and have the opportunity to use it in a safe, protected learning environment. They can do this using the workstation that they will normally use, and even do the learning in the workplace. It is difficult to imagine being closer to reality than this. With the appropriate support built into the training programme we have created an excellent learning environment.

**Learners work at their own pace**

It is very important that people learn at their own pace. Learning is something that cannot be forced, although there are those who think it can. In technology training, learners can work at a speed they choose. They do, in fact, control the learning process. It is important to remind them of this in the opening module of the programme.

Why is this factor so important? Perhaps we need to refer to the early chapters of this book on learning, in which I said that people all have inherent learning skills, but that they use them in quite different ways. Trying to predict how individuals learn is almost certain to fail. So we allow learners the freedom to learn as they wish.

Pace is an important factor in this. Some people will not progress until they are totally convinced that they have got the last step 'right'. They will do exercise after exercise until they are ready. Others will rush through the programme, even though they get things wrong, then they will return and go through it again. Some people even have the ability to skim through programmes very quickly and still gain a good understanding.

Chapter 8 on 'Understanding and communication', indicates some of the reasons why people need to learn at their own pace, without pressure. They need to feel comfortable and at ease with what they are doing, and nothing spoils this more than having to work at someone else's pace.

**Learners learn in the way they choose**

I like to learn my way, you like to learn your way, and everyone else likes to learn their way. Technology training gives us the scope to build programmes that allow people to learn exactly how they want to.
By using techniques such as learning maps learners can have the freedom to approach the learning as they want to. I have heard people argue that something as routine and technical as learning to use technology should follow a specific sequence. I totally disagree with this idea. Indeed certain people might want to follow such a sequence, but all learners shouldn't be forced to do the same. Freedom and choice in how we learn is an important ingredient of a good training programme and can be provided by good technology training.

**Learners are supported during learning**

During the learning process we all need support in the form of information, explanation, demonstrations, etc.

In technology training this support can be provided with a wide range of integrated sources of assistance. This support can be available as and when it is needed, making it even more powerful. Compare this to someone who is stuck during a training course and has to interrupt the teacher or wait for their turn to ask a question.

Integrated learning support is discussed in Chapter 9, on 'Continuous learning', and is a very successful part of technology training, provided the training designer recognizes the need for support and makes it available.

### Programmes are interesting and entertaining

Perhaps I should say that technology-based training *can be* interesting and entertaining. I have seen a great many programmes that are just the opposite. Technology provides so many possibilities that I fail to see how training designers can avoid making programmes interesting and entertaining, but somehow many do. The secret of maintaining interest and providing entertainment lies in the way the programme is structured.

In *The Business of Training* I describe how learning desire is stimulated through:

- exciting curiosity
- inviting involvement
- challenging perceptions
- feeding questioning minds
- providing opportunities for exploring and experimenting
- removing fear and embarrassment
- creating a safe, fun-filled environment

If these criteria are kept in the forefront of your mind during the design process it is perfectly possible to produce programmes that hold the learner's attention.

### Variety and flexibility are incorporated

Technology training is an ideal medium for providing variety and flexibility. There are so many ways that information, exercises and problems can be presented. In addition, there is such a wide scope for interacting with learners that the same approach need never be used twice. Naturally, what is possible depends to some extent on the hardware and software, but the major factor is the imagination of the training designer. I often review technology training programmes where the designer has used the same approach over and over again. I am bored after I have used it three times, and when I get to the tenth repeat I am ready to abort the whole process.

# Working with systems designers

For ten years before I became a trainer I worked as a systems designer. This has always helped me, because I understand the problems that systems designers have to deal with. By recognizing that most systems designers are delighted to produce simple easy-to-use systems, trainers can work with them to make it happen.

**Good systems are difficult to produce**

The first step in this is to accept that producing good functional systems is difficult, even when it is possible to get management to agree on what they want. It is difficult because the process of systems analysis, design and programming is complex. Add to this the fact that suitably skilled people are still in short supply, and those that are available have to work in a high-pressure environment, marked by time and money constraints, and you can see we are in a sensitive and explosive atmosphere.

By acknowledging the difficulty and by working closely with systems designers from the beginning of the project, it is possible, and perfectly feasible, that the systems design process can be made easier. Let me give an example.

---

I was working with a company on a new development. They were interested in building training into the new system. The systems designers were against it because of the extra work and complexity. After studying the requirements specification I was able to indicate several areas where changes could be made to simplify the system. When we looked at it in more detail, it became possible to make major changes that reduced the time and cost parameters for the system development. This included the fact that no manuals would have to be produced: all messages to users would be written by trainers and placed on a separate database, i.e. not programmed in the system, and error checks and control procedures could be simplified. The outcome was a close working relationship between trainers and systems designers and considerabe cost savings.

---

The approach to simplifying systems is not in itself difficult. It is only necessary to ask a series of questions about the reason for something, and the benefit the user will get from the feature, and one by one the simplifications appear.

**Counteract 'upside-down logic'**

Perhaps the most effective way to simplify a system is to analyse every instance of 'upside-down logic', and then suggest a way of dealing with each one. The result can be surprising. Here are two examples of how this can be done.

---

We made a request for a three-line message area to be used at the bottom of every screen. The first response was that this area was reserved for three separate lines to report the system responses. One line was for an error message, the next line for system condition messages, and the third line for default messages. This was clearly 'upside-down logic'. So I asked a simple question. Here is the dialogue that actually took place. I am Trevor and the systems designer is Sonia.

*Trevor*   Can error messages, system condition messages and default messages be displayed at the same time?
*Sonia*   No.
*Trevor*   So why not have all three lines designated for messages regardless of their type?
*Sonia*   Because users need to know which is which.
*Trevor*   Can we tell them which is which by displaying the words ACTION (I don't like the word 'error'), SYSTEM CONDITION and DEFAULT?
*Sonia*   Well, we could, but it uses up too much space.
*Trevor*   Yes, but we would have three lines now for each message.
*Sonia*   Well, in that case it might be possible. I will have to check.

After checking it became possible.

---

The second example concerns the same system, but a different systems designer. I wanted to present several types of message in the new three-line message area. Here again is the dialogue.

---

*Trevor*   I would like to display a message on request about the field that the user is working on. That means that when users press F1 they will get a helpful message.
*Paul*   Yes, but the three-line area is for computer messages.
*Trevor*   Yes, that's what I want. A message from a database that refers to the field being used, and which will be displayed when users press F1.
*Paul*   Wow, that's going to take some doing.
*Trevor*   Why?
*Paul*   Well, we are going to have to rewrite all the programs to cater for this additional transaction, and there's no way I can get that passed.
*Trevor*   What if we just used the screen ID (every screen has an identity ID, and a number for the field) and the field reference to look up a database?
*Paul*   That's not part of the specification.
*Trevor*   OK, but could you do it?
*Paul*   Yes, I guess so.
*Trevor*   How much effort?
*Paul*   Well, virtually nothing. We already have all the IDs and we only need a simple look-up code attached to F1 and we've cracked it.
*Trevor*   So can we go ahead?
*Paul*   What about all the messages?
*Trevor*   Oh, that's OK, training will produce them.
*Paul*   OK, I'll check with the powers that be and get back to you.

---

These two examples demonstrate that the logic as seen from the systems designer's viewpoint is different, usually upside down, from the viewpoint of the user. In the above examples there is good reason for the systems logic. It is just necessary to question it from the other direction.

### Difficulty increases in direct proportion to the lack of desire

This is Bentley's law of prevarication. I have found that when people don't want to do something they can think up the most wonderful excuses (sorry, reasons) for not doing it. My first question when people, especially systems designers, say something is difficult is to ask them why they don't want to do it. They usually tell me the reason, which is frequently time, workload, cost, or something similar. I then ask whether the task would be possible if the reason for not wanting to do it was removed. This nearly always leads to a discussion about how we can do it, and this in turn usually indicates that what I have asked for is not so difficult after all. If I can then help to ease the pressure on the systems designer, I am home and dry. The key is—**Don't fight, help.**

### Don't become enchanted by technology

When I was a systems designer and leading a team on a large project, I always had a simple rule for dealing with 'user representatives'—**Get them on our side**. This quite simply meant enchanting them with the technology. We would send them on courses, train them in the systems design process, even sit them with programmers. Soon they would be busy 'helping' to develop the system. Their role as user representatives was completely usurped.

Of course, I later learned that this was a counterproductive strategy, but many systems designers still use it, and I know trainers who, though they would deny it, have become enchanted with technology.

My advice is to keep your feet on the ground and continue asking those seemingly silly questions. When someone answers with 'you wouldn't understand' say 'try me', and nine times out of ten you'll discover it's because they can't explain.

### If it isn't simple and easy to use, it won't work

This is a well-known law for designers in general, but one that apparently doesn't apply to systems designers. As I am writing this, using my Amstrad PC, I am aware of my quick tips card positioned on the top of my keyboard. One of the statements on it reads as follows:

Cut    | Alt |   +   | − |    or    | Ctrl |   +   | F4 |

I suppose there is a certain logic in using the minus sign for 'cut', but why give me an alternative that is less obvious? There is another tip that says:

Enter printer control    | * |    or    | Ctrl |   +   | F10 |

Now this is even more ludicrous because the alternative is so much more effort. Fortunately, I have learned how to use the PC (please don't ask me how) so I understand these statements, but they are neither simple nor easy to use.

This problem abounds in the world of technology. Perhaps the main reason is that people who work in computer and systems design are so well versed in technology, if not actually suffering from gadget disease, that they just cannot see what causes us poor mortals any difficulty. Regardless of the cause, the solution lies in questioning the need for everything, and never stopping until the outcome is very simple, and hence easy to use. This, of course, means it will also be easy to learn.

## Key points

- Technology used properly is a powerful learning medium.
- There are six main reasons for this:
  —the learning environment is close to reality;
  —learners work at their own pace;
  —learners learn in the way they want to;
  —they are supported during learning;
  —programs are interesting and entertaining;
  —there is plenty of variety and flexibility.
- People learn best in an environment as close as possible to real life.
- In technology training, learners control the learning process and work at the speed they prefer.
- In technology training, support can be provided with a wide range of integrated sources of assistance.
- Technology provides so many possibilities that training designers can hardly avoid making programmes that are interesting and entertaining.
- Technology training is an ideal medium for providing variety and flexibility.
- Good systems are difficult to produce.
- 'Upside-down logic' should be counteracted.
- Difficulty increases in direct proportion to the lack of desire.
- Don't become enchanted by technology.
- If it isn't simple and easy to use, it won't work.

---

### PRACTICAL APPLICATION

- **Technology training is only really limited by the imagination of the training designer.**
- **During the design stage of the programme development, consider carefully the six factors discussed in this chapter. Ask yourself: 'How well have I used the technology to capitalize on its power and effectiveness?'**
- **Make an effort to get to know the systems designers; find out the kind of problems they have and see if you can help.**
- **Follow the five steps for working with systems designers, and tell them what the five steps are.**
- **And once again: If it isn't simple and easy to use, it won't work.**

---

# 12 Simulations

The use of simulations in training has been a growing trend, particularly in technological areas. The idea of building a simulation of some working environment has been used in a variety of ways from flight simulators for pilot training to wind tunnels for simulating the effects of the environment on models of all shapes and sizes.

A simulation can be described as an imitation of reality. In training, the closer we can get to reality in the learning environment, the quicker learners will move along the learning curve. For simulations to work they need to have the following characteristics:

- They should represent reality so that learners are unaware they are using a simulation.
- Learners must be able to stop the simulation to receive feedback.
- The simulation is robust enough to cope with accidental or deliberate misuse.
- The use of the simulation can be monitored and outcomes recorded.
- The simulation can be readily and easily amended to match changes in the real world.

## Representing reality

There is often confusion between an exercise and a simulation. Here are my definitions:

**Simulation**   An exact replica of the situation learners will meet in the working environment, or as near a facsimile as can be produced.

**Exercise**   An opportunity to practise the application of knowledge and the development of skills in a way that does not exactly replicate the working environment.

There are four main ways in which I have seen and experienced simulations in technology training. I will discuss these in the order in which they most directly represent reality.

The first of these is the use of the real 'live' system, together with an extensive embedded training and support system. In fact, this would not be a simulation except that the database used is a special 'training' database. Learners use the same system to learn from that they will be using in the workplace. The one other difference between this simulation and the workplace is that the training will probably be done in a training centre.

The second level of simulation also uses the real 'live' system, but without the embedded training and support, which is provided instead by a facility running alongside, or concurrent with the 'live' system. In this case, learners know that the guidance they receive is coming from a separate system that might or might not be available when they are working. This approach is quite close to the embedded method, but the concurrent system has to be very carefully maintained to keep it in-line with the 'live' system.

---

I helped a building society to develop a concurrent system which was designed as follows. The 'live' system was used in 'training mode', i.e. with a training database. A separate, in this example, audio and paper-based system was prepared to guide learners through the 'live' system. The synchronization of the audio training pack was carefully timed, but audio signals were included to help learners know where they were on the tape. The training was done a week before the scheduled 'going live' date, and it was done in the branches using the same equipment and system that staff would use when working. It was very successful.

---

The third approach is the use of off-line CBT, i.e. a computer-based programme that includes a simulation of all or part of the 'live' system. The programmes are produced using a CBT authoring package. The best of these can import screens from the 'live' system and simulate the functionality of these screens. These off-line approaches can be developed before the 'live' system is available, and can actually help in the final design of the 'live' system. The main problems are in keeping the simulated system up to date with the 'live' system, and in presenting learners with exactly what they will see when they are using the 'live' system.

The last of the four approaches is the classroom environment where people are guided through the use of the 'live' system. This may be done using the 'live' system, or a simulation of it. This is a very popular approach. Naturally, the environment is neither a good simulation of the working environment, nor is it real because guidance is received from a teacher. There are other problems in terms of the lack of opportunity for learners to work at their own pace, and the sense of competition which classrooms always engender, both of which are counterproductive to successful learning.

There is no doubt that the closer the training is to reality the better the simulation will be, particularly in terms of its learning effectiveness.

## Simulations and feedback

When using a simulation the results of learners' actions should be clearly demonstrated and explained, and learners need to be able to stop the simulation and seek information about their progress. The more automated the simulation is, the more difficult it is to build in this kind of monitoring and feedback. It can be done, but it will require very clear thinking on the part of the training designer to predict the likely needs of learners.

It is in the area of feedback that the classroom approach probably scores the highest, except that it is unlikely that everyone can get the feedback they want when they want it. Perhaps the concurrent approach offers one of the best combinations of automation and feedback, but here the problem is that users are learning from a system that won't be fully available to them in the workplace.

The key to successful feedback can be analysed as:

- continuous monitoring of learner activity;
- a 'rewind' facility to see what learners have done;
- a 'fast-forward' facility to show what the result of the action will be;
- 'start again' and 'replay' facilities.

These might sound difficult to supply, but their provision can and should be made. The software and hardware are available; all it needs is for training designers to know what is required and to think creatively and innovate.

## Coping with misuse

I have never been able to predict or provide for the wilful imagination or thoughtlessness of learners, especially when they are presented with a carefully designed simulation. It is essential, therefore, that the simulation can cope with whatever learners throw at it.

---

In the example of the building society quoted above, we discovered a fault in the 'live' system because one of the trainees decided to try to draw out more money than was in the account. The system accepted it and produced a minus balance in the passbook. None of the examples in the training transactions were set up to do this because we never thought an operator would ever try to do it.

---

Simulations do, therefore, have to cope, as we hope the 'live' system would, with such actions and give the learners meaningful messages so that they can learn from mistakes, or any attempts they make to misuse the system. This also gives them confidence in the system itself. If the 'live' system is not used as a part of the simulation, it often happens that learners are disappointed when they discover that the 'live' system does not work as well as the simulation.

## Monitoring and recording

In the previous section on feedback there is reference to monitoring the way learners are using the simulation. This monitoring process is essential in providing useful feedback.

The monitoring that can take place is concerned with (a) what learners do; (b) the mistakes they make; (c) the use they make of the training and support system; and (d) the results they achieve.

All these can be recorded. In fact, it is necessary to monitor and keep records of (a), (b) and (d) for audit purposes, so this facility should be built into the 'live' system as a matter of course. Element (c) should be an essential part of the user-support system, which is fully operational while the simulation is in use.

The monitoring should be recorded and held in a file for the particular learner involved; this is quite possible by keeping a note of the learner's 'log in' password. Such files can be maintained temporarily while training is in operation, or for future reference. (However, if we are concerned with the success of the training it is probably necessary only to keep personal records temporarily.) These can be accumulated to provide statistics of the overall success of the training simulation.

## Synchronization

Perhaps the most difficult aspect of using simulations is keeping them in harmony with the real world. When the 'live' system is used as a fundamental element of the simulation, this is essential and virtually cannot be avoided. With other forms of simulation it is more likely, and more usual, for simulations to get out of 'sync' with the real world. This is often excused as 'being close enough not to matter', and the cost and time it takes to maintain harmony makes this a very attractive excuse.

If simulations are to be used then they *must* be kept completely synchronized with the real system, otherwise they are a waste of time and effort in the first place. Unless we can make simulations a close replica of the real world we might as well tell learners that the system works 'more or less' like this, and from a training and performance support perspective this is completely useless.

## Key points

• Simulations should replicate reality as closely as possible.
• To do this they can be embedded, concurrent, off-line or classroom.
• Feedback is essential to successful simulations.
• Learners should be able to rewind, fast-forward, start again and replay simulations.
• Accidental and deliberate misuse should be catered for.
• Monitoring and recording of the use of simulations is essential.
• It should be possible to see what learners have done, the mistakes they have made, the use they made of the support system, and the results they achieved.
• Keeping the simulation in 'sync' with the live system is vital to the successful use of simulations.

> ## PERSONAL APPLICATION
>
> - Ensure that the simulation looks and feels like the real thing.
> - Try to avoid providing features that will not be available in the real system. If the real system is in monochrome, then don't use colour in the simulation.
> - If colours are used in the simulation make sure they match the real system.
> - Provide exactly the same error messages.
> - Don't try to improve the simulation to overcome defects in the real system. Try to persuade the developers to change the real system.
> - Don't use features, such as graphics, in the training if they don't exist in the real system.
> - Establish a means by which the communication of changes in the real world can be received and used to adapt the simulation.

# 13 Performance support systems

Because I am writing about technology the kind of performance support systems that I will deal with will be the electronic version. Everyone who works, i.e. has to perform, has a performance support system. Sometimes these are clearly defined, understood and useful, and sometimes they are totally inadequate. They can include the use of manuals, training, the advice of supervisors, suggestions from colleagues, and written job descriptions and objectives.

Electronic performance support systems (EPSS) attempt to provide the support and help people need, when they need it, through the terminal they use in their daily work. In *The Business of Training* Gloria Geary describes electronic performance support systems as follows:

An electronic performance support system is an integrated electronic environment that is available to, and easily accessible by, each employee. It is structured to provide immediate, individualised on-line access to the full range of information, software, guidance, advice and assistance, data, images, tools, and assessment and monitoring systems to permit employees to perform their jobs with a minimum of support and intervention by others.

An electronic performance support system is not a piece of software or an electronic device. It is a concept about the provision of information to users in a way that enables them to perform better, and to make full use of the capabilities of the systems they are using. It has been estimated that most systems are only used up to about one-fifth of their capabilities. This might be sufficient for the users' needs, but what a waste it is. It is also estimated that fewer than 30 per cent of computer users reach the highly skilled category, and that most just manage to reach basic competency. There is obviously a need for effective performance support.

## 'Reason of use' approach

In the past, if users wanted information about what they were doing they had three courses of action: look up a manual; ask a colleague; or ask a supervisor. This is still largely the case in many organizations. With the advent of complex computer systems, this approach to getting support began to flounder. First, the manuals were unreadable and, second, colleagues and supervisors had the same problems in knowing what was happening. To overcome this, some organizations set up 'help-desks' that users could ring if they were stuck. Then software producers began to include information as part of the system.

Unfortunately, the help-desks and the help-information provided by the system were not very helpful. This was because users were unable to get the information they wanted unless they knew what to ask for.

The first step towards a more efficient method of meeting information needs was the production of 'context-sensitive' support information. This approach provided information about the work that users were doing at the time they requested help. This was a big improvement, but it still didn't answer users' real needs. Then came the breakthrough. It was realized that the way information was organized and presented followed the same 'upside-down logic' I have talked about earlier. Information about the system was provided on a subject or sequence-oriented basis. But when users want help, they come for it from the opposite direction; they may not even know the subject, and the sequence is usually irrelevant to them. In other words, the manuals and help-systems were doing everything backwards. Add to this the fact that the information was organized in a linear way, i.e. from high-level abstraction to low-level detail, and you can see that users would have great difficulty finding what they wanted.

This change of thinking led to the development of a new approach to organizing support information. I call this new approach the 'reason of use' approach.

The 'reason of use' approach provides a variety of paths to the same information, and organizes information in 'interest blocks'. Here is an example to clarify what I mean.

---

In most gazetteers for a city, theatres are listed in one section and restaurants in another. Neither is linked to the other. If I am lucky there might be a map showing both, but it is more likely that there will be two maps located in the different sections. What I want is to find a vegetarian restaurant near to the theatre I am going to.

If a 'reason of use' approach had been used, the designer of the gazetteer would find a way to link the two pieces of information. This could be done by providing all the information about the city in geographical areas with a reference to more detailed sections containing information about theatres and restaurants. In this case, I would look up the theatre, find the geographical area it is in, turn to the area information, find references to restaurants, then go to the restaurant section and, bingo, I find what I want.

Another approach might be to provide information about theatres in alphabetical order, and give for each theatre a list of nearest stations, bus routes, car parks, restaurants, etc., working on the basis that this is the kind of information people want when going to the theatre.

---

This approach can be applied to any information structure, but it means that we have to approach the way we produce support information differently from the way we have been used to doing it. Unfortunately, this need to change our approach to organizing information is not widely understood. I have seen examples where people have put existing but badly organized manuals on-line in the hope that the speed and power of the technology will resolve the problem. The result has been chaos.

# Building EPSS

Any organization using computer technology can build electronic performance support systems (EPSS). The exact approach will depend on the hardware and software they are using, but it can be done. There are five main steps:

- Analyse users' support needs.
- Define access needs.
- Develop the information approach.
- Prepare the performance support resources.
- Design and build the interface between the application systems and the performance support resources.

## Users' support needs

In Chapter 3 I discussed the kind of support that learners would need when using a new system. All this type of support is relevant as part of the performance support system, but in addition we need to think about the needs of competent and highly skilled users. These needs can fall into six main categories:

- background information
- context-sensitive specific information
- data
- rules, controls and procedures
- electronic tools
- advice and assistance

**Background information** This is the information concerning the environment in which work takes place. In a bank this might include such things as the current base interest rate, economic trends, stock market information, and so on. It is likely that this information will change, and so access will be needed frequently.

**Context-sensitive information** When people are working on a specific task, they may have specific information needs. In a building society this might include such things as closing an account because the account holder has died. This is not necessarily a daily event so the operator might need information on what to do. This category also includes information on how to correct errors in the context of the work being done.

**Data** When using technology it is often necessary to input data such as currency codes, post codes, etc. Such data can be quite extensive. Rather than expect staff to memorize it, the performance support system can provide them with tables of data from which they can select the appropriate code.

**Rules, controls and procedures** Most organizations lay down procedures about the way that work has to be done. This is essential for the orderly, accurate and appropriate functioning of the organization. These rules, controls and procedures are extensive and need to be observed. Once again it is unreasonable to expect people to remember them all, and so with a performance support system we can offer access to this information, either task-specific or general.

**Electronic tools**   Many computer systems now offer on-line tools such as calculators, spreadsheets, graphics, etc. These can be linked into the performance support system and made available either as job-specific or general aids.

**Advice and assistance**   It is perfectly possible to produce expert systems that advise staff what to do. These can function either automatically or on request. I have worked with a system which provides bank staff with advice on checking a client's suitability for a loan. I have also designed a simple system that triggered a sales response on the screen when the amount in a customer's account exceeded a certain amount.

There may be more areas of support needed in special situations, but those above cover the majority of areas of need.

**Access needs**   It is important to define the various levels of access before the performance support system is built. I break these down into five categories:

- immediate automatic feedback
- immediate context-sensitive data
- immediate requested information
- learning materials (training)
- reference information

**Immediate automatic feedback**   As it indicates, this is the fastest level of access and is particularly relevant when displaying action (error), messages to users. It should happen as soon as the data is input, or as soon as users attempt to process the screen.

**Immediate context-sensitive data**   This should be displayed as soon as possible after a request, preferably in a window on the screen. It should also be possible for users to select the data in the window and transfer it to the screen they are working on. This is what I call the 'sticky cursor'.

**Immediate requested information**   This should be displayed as soon as possible, and while users are still working on the task concerned. The information on closing an account due to a death would be of this kind, because without it users would be unable to continue.

**Learning materials**   Ideally, learning materials should be presented as soon as the task is completed, or when users have time to complete the learning. Reinforcing information, or memory-jogging items, should be provided via one of the above three 'immediate' levels.

**Reference information**   This could be looked up at leisure, either when the task is completed or when users have time to absorb the information. If the task could not be completed without the information, then it should be in one of the 'immediate' levels.

Perhaps the key to establishing access level is the priority of need. This can be decided in each organization, but three priorities could be:

- speedy and accurate task completion;
- performance enhancement, e.g. marketing support;
- personal development.

**Information approach**

The overall approach will be the 'reason of use' method, but this needs to be defined for each type of information and the structure agreed before the support resources are constructed. This involves deciding on the most appropriate access methods. I like to work with four approaches in mind: backwards; forwards, sideways; and upside-down.

These four approaches allow me to move from where I am to where I can find the information I need. In a book, for example, I can only move forwards and backwards, and I have the contents and perhaps an index to help me. A computer environment presents me with more options than this.

**Backwards**   I often find when I am working on the computer or reading a book that I want to retrace my steps to find information that led me to where I am. I can do this by browsing back through the information, or by going directly back to the specific information I want. With modern computer facilities I can do this by selecting key words, or by bringing up an index in a window on the screen. This makes access quick and efficient, and I don't lose the place where I am.

**Forwards**   This is finding information about where I am going, rather than where I have come from. There might be a number of options open to me, and I could want information on each of them to help me make a choice. Learning maps are one example, and flowcharts are another.

**Sideways**   Whatever I am doing when I am working there are always parallel subjects/activities that could be of interest to me. In sequentially organized information I can go backwards and forwards, but I am unable to move across into a parallel stream of information. It is like a motorway and railway line running next to each other and having the option to move from one to the other, which in real life would be difficult, if not impossible. On a computer it is not only possible, it is relatively easy. Once we have moved sideways we can then go backwards and forwards in the new stream.

**Upside-down**   Imagine that you are serving customers in a bank and they want to know how much it will cost them to borrow £2000. You can look up the information and tell them. They might respond that it is too expensive, so you can turn the question over and ask them how much they want to pay each month and then calculate how much they can borrow. This search for information by going in the opposite or reverse way is what I describe as upside-down. I spend many hours explaining to computer programmers that error messages should not say why things are wrong, but how they can be put right.

**Support resources**     The creation of the resources involves the putting together of the infor-mation, data, etc. This will mean the collection, writing and organizing of the information, as well as the access links that will be provided. There are three key elements involved:

- collecting the appropriate information, etc.
- writing and organizing the resources;
- preparing the cross-reference links.

**Collecting information**    This can be a time-consuming task, but it is a vital one, for the success of performance support depends entirely on the appropriateness of the contents of the resources. The process should not be cut short, and the information should be collected entirely from the perspective of users, i.e. how to use the system, and not how it works.

**Writing and organizing the resources**    It is imperative that the people responsible for this task are skilled in writing simple, direct, learning-centred information. This is then organized in accordance with the deci-sions made about users' needs and access methods and levels. It is probably better to think in terms of small, linked databases rather than one gigantic database containing everything.

**Preparing cross-reference links**    However the resources are organized, it is necessary to produce a system to link elements of information together. This might be done by starting with a simple framework based on the 'reason of use' method. When we are in need of information, if we know where we are starting from, we can usually define it in terms of information that is more general; more detailed; probably of interest; and, possibly of interest.

We can then construct the performance support system to present us with these options when we ask for them. The framework is depicted as follows (Fig. 13.1).

**Interface**    The production of the interface between the application system and the performance support system will depend on the software and hardware, but approaches could include:

- embedded
- concurrent
- related

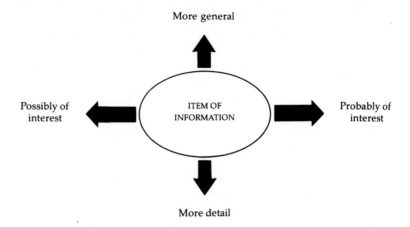

More general

Possibly of
interest

ITEM OF
INFORMATION

Probably of
interest

More detail

**Figure 13.1**  *A framework for linking elements of information*

- linked
- separated

**Embedded**  Means that the performance support system is actually
built into the application system, of which it is an integral part.

**Concurrent**  When two systems run side by side and interact they are
said to be working concurrently.

**Related**  This is a separate system which may be called upon to pass
information to the system being worked on, and vice versa. While one
system is working, the other is dormant, waiting.

**A linked approach**  Means that separate systems can be connected
through a buffer system, which works as an interface between the two.

**Separated**  Just as it sounds, this means that the systems are separate
and the interface is provided by giving users information about accessing the other system.

Some or all of these approaches can be used in creating the performance
support system. It is not necessary to spend a fortune making everything
embedded or concurrent. The needs will determine the best approach
when linked with the available hardware and software.

## Key points

- Electronic performance support systems (EPSS) are not pieces of software or electronic devices. They are a concept based on new thinking.
- This change of thinking has led to the development of a new
  approach to organizing information—the 'reason of use' approach.
- There are five main steps in building EPSS:
  —analyse users' support needs;
  —define access needs;

—develop the information approach;
—prepare the performance support resources;
—design and build the EPSS interface.
- User support needs fall into six main categories:
—background information
—context-sensitive specific information
—date
—rules, controls and procedures
—electronic tools
—advice and assistance
- The five categories of performance support access are:
—immediate automatic feedback
—immediate context-sensitive data
—immediate requested information
—learning materials (training)
—reference information
- There are four main ways of accessing support information: backwards; forwards; sideways; and upside-down.
- There are three key elements involved in preparing EPSS resources:
—collecting the appropriate information, etc.
—writing and organizing the resources;
—preparing the cross-reference links.
- Producing the interface between the application system and the performance support system depends on the software and hardware, but approaches could include: embedded; concurrent; related; linked; and separated.

---

### PRACTICAL APPLICATION

The whole of this chapter is about the practical application of EPSS, so in this summary I will re-emphasize the main points.

- **Work closely with systems designers—you need their help and support to make EPSS work. Be constructive, not confrontational.**
- **Think about EPSS entirely from the user's point of view; remember to counteract 'upside-down logic'.**
- **Be prepared to write all the EPSS resources. You need the information, anyway, to produce good learning materials so why not produce all of it, including the computer-generated messages.**
- **Put all information and messages in databases, definitely not in the system's computer programs.**
- **Follow the 'reason of use' approach for organizing information, not only in EPSS, but in all learning materials.**
- **Make all the information in the EPSS 'learning-centred', so that it is a learning resource as well as information.**
- **Go for the simplest and easiest ways of doing things, especially in creating the EPSS interface.**

# 14 Making technology training successful

There are a lot of things to think about when designing good technology training, and I have tried to deal with all of them in this book. In each chapter I have attempted to give advice and suggestions for how to make technology training successful. In this chapter I want to concentrate on what I believe are the four keys to success, without reducing the importance of what has been said in earlier chapters. The keys are:

- Emphasize the learning, not the technology.
- Give learners all the power and control.
- Provide intelligent interactivity and feedback when learners want it.
- Go about everything in the simplest and easiest way possible.

## Emphasis on learning

The technology is a means to an end—in this case, helping people to learn. It is not important in itself. The training programme should play down the use of the technology as a learning aid. Such comments as 'In order to get the best out of this programme you will need to familiarize yourself with the keyboard' is a definite put-off. The use of the technology should be so simple that training or information about using it becomes unnecessary.

I have just reviewed a technology training programme. The first ten pages of the accompanying guide described the equipment I needed, explained about loading disks, told me I would need to use the specified keyboard, and explained how to log on. The emphasis was on technology and more technology. Nowhere in those ten pages did it state what the programme was about, what I could learn from it, or the fun and excitement I would have using it.

I need to know what to do to use the programme, but this should come later, with a comment such as: 'Now, when you are ready, load the disk and type START. If you are not sure about loading the disk, turn to page 23 and follow the simple guide.'

The technology should never be allowed to impinge on the learning process. Even when the subject of the training programme is technology it should be simplified and described in terms of the purpose of the task, not the way the technology works. Here is an example of what I mean.

*Task: Opening an account*

To open an account you will need to enter the customer's name (maximum 30 characters) in the first field, then the address, followed by the postcode.

The system will check that the postcode is present and falls within the correct range.

This explains the way the system works and the limits that users will have to observe. It is instructive. In the following example the emphasis is on the task.

Opening an account for a customer means that you will need to type in the customer's name, address and postcode. The postcode is quite important for correspondence and statistical purposes, so if the customer doesn't know it, look it up on the file.

From a learning perspective the second example is much better than the first; it is much more conversational and easier to understand. Learners do not need spoon-feeding, providing the system has been designed to facilitate easy use. Even when the system being learned is poorly designed there is no reason to carry this through to the training.

## Learner control

Whether you like it or not, learners are already in control of their own learning, so why pretend? Why not accept it and hand them control of their use of the training programme? When I am learning and I feel that I can do what I want, e.g. I can skip a section, or ignore an exercise, it gives me a strong feeling of freedom and power. This is good for me. However, I am aware that some people want more direction than others. So we should build all technology training programmes to give a wide choice, and to give learners the power to do what they want.

I recently used a programme which at the end of each module had a test. The test was of the multi-choice question variety. On the first module I deliberately selected the most obviously wrong answers. The programme asked me to try again. I did the same thing, the programme then told me that I would have to review the module and complete the test correctly before I could continue.

This is not only a very poor learning approach, but it takes all control and power away from learners, and it becomes a battle between learners and the system. How much better it would have been if at the end of the module I had been given a choice of selecting an exercise which I thought would help me to consolidate my understanding, or just be allowed to continue if I felt I understood what I had learned.

## Interactivity

From beginning to end of the training programme it is important to provide a means for learners to respond to the programme, and to get intelligent feedback. This should be possible at any time. If learners are in the middle of a module they should be able to switch out of it into some level of dialogue with the programme. In Chapter 10, 'Using technology to overcome technology limitations', I mentioned some ways of responding to learners' questions.

Interactivity is more than this—it is about reacting to the needs of learners. Not telling them what they need to do, but asking if they would like some help. Not giving them the correct answer after they have got it wrong three times, but suggesting that they might want to look at a worked example. We must try to remember that it is up to learners to decide how much they want to struggle with their learning. Giving unwanted help does not, in fact, help.

The key then is to provide the opportunity for learners to exit from where they are in the programme and to move into a different part of the programme to engage in some interaction. Alternatively, they can be given the freedom to engage in interaction from wherever they happen to be in the programme.

The good training designer knows that what is important is the way the programme reacts to learners, and not the other way round. So thinking intelligently about the kind of reactions we would demand from the programme if we were learners will help us to create good interactive training programmes. Incidentally, pressing the space bar to continue is not interaction.

## Simplicity

People who have attended my workshops know that I always put up a saying on the wall. It is about simplicity and helps me to remember that:

**It is easy to make things difficult**
**But difficult to make things easy**

Difficult it may be, but it is always worthwhile to attempt to make the system and the learning as easy as possible. If something doesn't seem easy to me, even if I understand it, I always question it and seek to find an easier way.

## Key points

- There are four keys to success in training technology:
  —Emphasize the learning not the technology.
  —Give learners all the power and control.
  —Provide intelligent interactivity and feedback when learners want it.
  —Make everything simple and easy.
- The technology is a means to an end—in this case, helping people to learn. It is not important in itself.
- Give learners control of their learning and the way they use the programme.
- Provide a means for learners to respond to the programme, and to get intelligent feedback at any time.

- What is important is the way the programme reacts to learners, not the other way round.
- The simplest approach is always the best and the easiest.

---

**PRACTICAL APPLICATION**

- Careful, thorough analysis.
- Thoughtful, intuitive design.
- Intelligent understanding of learning needs.
- Taking the learner's viewpoint.
- Giving maximum choice and freedom to learners.
- Doing everything in the simplest way possible.

# User guides

Why user guides? I believe this book to be a useful and practical guide to meeting the technology challenge, but I have added a set of user guides to its contents at the end. The reason is simple and, I hope, easy to understand. When I read a book, particularly of this type, I always feel that I need to make a list of all the key things that I can use in my day-to-day work. Sometimes I even do this and stick the lists on the wall. So, to save you the effort, or at least to give you my idea of the key points, I have produced seven lists that you might find useful. These are:

1 Principles of good technology-based training
2 The four learning styles
3 Supporting learning
4 Overcoming technology learning barriers
5 Feedback
6 Building good technology-based training
7 Building performance support systems

**PRINCIPLES OF GOOD TECHNOLOGY-BASED TRAINING**

Good technology-based training is learning-centred.

Learning is voluntary and needs to be motivated.

Technology training programmes should be short and simple, and enable learners to be successful.

Minimize the technology aspects of the learning.

Patronizing learners, either by the language used or by the way the programme interacts with them, detracts from the programme and makes it ineffective.

A high degree of interaction between learners and the programme is essential, with the emphasis on how the programme responds to learners, rather than vice versa.

Provide challenging, problem-solving feedback.

## THE FOUR LEARNING STYLES

**Informed learning**—with the emphasis on developing concepts.

(*Conceptualizing*)

**Experimental learning**—with the emphasis on trying out.

(*Experimenting*)

**Exploratory learning**—with the emphasis on discovery and experience.

(*Experiencing*)

**Analytical learning**—with the emphasis on thinking.

(*Reflecting*)

*It is the application of information within a meaningful experience in the learner's environment that enables learning to take place.*

**SUPPORTING LEARNING**

**Information**    in whatever form, is more readily understood if it is provided in answer to a question.

**Examples**    help learners to seek information and enable them to fit everything into the context of what they have observed.

**Exercises**    give confidence, when completed successfully, and provide a basis for practice and evaluating learning progress.

**Guidance**    constantly gives signposts and directions so that learners will be able to steer their own learning path.

**Support**    means providing help and encouragement when learners want it and in a way that motivates them to continue.

## OVERCOMING TECHNOLOGY LEARNING BARRIERS

Shift the emphasis from system functionality to system usability.

Never willingly accept the limits imposed by systems—always try to remove them.

Encourage operators to concentrate on working at the speed that suits them and the customer—not to please the computer.

Train managers in the skills of supporting and helping people to learn.

Classroom-style training is the least effective, and yet the most widely used approach to training. Counteract this example of 'upside-down logic'.

Remove psychological barriers by:

- converting the unknown into the known
- encouraging people to concentrate on their strengths
- developing positive motivation

Make learning enjoyable and effective by providing learners with the opportunity to:

- choose what and how to learn
- experiment
- self-monitor learning

## FEEDBACK

Good feedback is helpful, encouraging, positive and progressive.

Feedback is helpful and reinforces learning when it reiterates what has happened and makes a useful statement.

Encouraging feedback is information that supports the progress learners are making.

Positive feedback gives success rates, not error rates, and helps to assess learning progress.

Progressive feedback moves learners forward.

Everything is aimed at making it easy and comfortable for people to learn to use the technology. Far from being a 'soft option' this approach is a powerful learning-centred technique that speeds up learning and considerably improves performance.

### BUILDING GOOD TECHNOLOGY-BASED TRAINING

Provide choice in how and what to learn by:

- open questions
- random selection
- descriptive menus
- learning maps

The success of technology-based training depends to a large extent on the quality, simplicity, and ease of use of the human/machine interface.

Give learners freedom and control over their own learning.

Provide constant support and information, exploration and demonstrations, but only when requested by learners.

The key to good responses from systems designers is: **Help them don't fight them.**

The four keys to success are:

- emphasize the learning, not the technology;
- give learners total power and control;
- provide intelligent interactive feedback when learners want it;
- do everything in the simplest, easiest way possible.

**BUILDING PERFORMANCE SUPPORT SYSTEMS**

Use the 'reason of use' approach for the structure of information resources.

The five steps for building performance support systems are:

- analyse user support needs
- define access needs
- develop information approach
- prepare performance support resources
- design and build performance support interface

Three suggested support priorities are:

1 speedy, accurate task completion
2 performance enhancement
3 personal development

Performance support resources can be embedded, concurrent, related, linked or separated.

# Suggested reading

Bach, Richard (1978) *Illusions*, London: Pan Books.
   A small and powerful commentary on the human search for personal power.
Bach, Richard (1973) *Jonathan Livingstone Seagull*, London: Pan Books.
   The ultimate quest for personal power and the removal of limits to our
   capabilities and performance. Everyone in human resource development
   should read this book.
Bentley, Trevor J. (1990) *The Business of Training*, Maidenhead: McGraw-Hill.
   A companion book to this one.
Bentley, Trevor J. (1991) *The Management Services Handbook*, London: Pitman.
   Has a very good section on human resource development and a wide cross-
   section of topics of interest to those in business.
Bentley, Trevor J. (1987) *Report Writing in Business*, London: Kogan Page.
   A short purposeful book on providing effective and practical reports. A useful
   guide to simple clear writing.
Dolmas, Joseph S. (1988) *Designing User Interfaces for Software*, New York: Prentice-
   Hall.
   A useful guide to the key requirements for producing good human/machine
   interfaces.
Geary, Gloria (1988) *Making CBT Happen*, Boston: Weingarten.
   An excellent book. It is clear about the advantages and disadvantages of
   CBT, and gives a good guide to how to use CBT effectively.
Geary, Gloria (1991) *Electronic Performance Support Systems*, Boston: Weingarten.
   This is a very good book for those building or about to build EPSS. Gloria
   echoes my views on learning and highlights reasons why human performance
   is well below what society needs and wants. There are a dozen extensive case
   studies that give much food for thought.
Gibran, Kahlil (1980) *The Prophet*, London: Heinemann.
   The famous and essential guide for anyone working with people, particularly
   in a learning environment. One of my favourite books.
Gowers, Sir Ernest (1973) *The Complete Plain Words*, London: Pelican.
   This book should be on the bookshelf of anyone who writes anything, partic-
   ularly those who need to produce clear simple messages from which people
   can learn.
Kopp, Simon (1988) *If You Meet the Buddha on the Road Kill Him*, London:
   Sheldon Press.
   An essential book for people seeking to develop and grow, and who also
   want to share what they learn with others.
Millman, Don (1984) *The Way of the Peaceful Warrior*, Tiburon: H. J. Kramer Inc.
   This book is about a journey of self-discovery and learning in a world that
   tries to force us into a particular mould. Good for the aspiring trainer.

Rogers, Carl (1983) *Freedom to Learn for the 80's*, Columbus: Charles E. Merrill.
This book has inspired much of my work over the past few years—essential reading for all trainers.

Strassmann, Paul A. (1985) *Information Payoff*, New York: Free Press.
The expansion of the information society, using as it does the new computer technology, can be frightening and awe-inspiring unless we understand the values of good information. This book helps us to do this.

Strunk, William and E. B. White (1979) *The Elements of Style*, New York: Macmillan.
The essential guide to clear concise writing.

Ta-Kao, Ch'u (1986) *Tao Te Ching*, London: Unwin.
The way. The path to follow to self-development and self-realization.

Wurman, Richard Saul (1989) *Information Anxiety*, New York: Doubleday.
'Information anxiety . . . is the black hole between data and knowledge, and it happens when information doesn't tell us what we want or need to know.' If you are planning to write the information support for performance support systems read this book first.

# Appendix: Assessing and evaluating technology-based training (TBT)

This appendix contains three parts:

- a definition of good TBT;
- a sample assessment report on three TBT programmes;
- an explanation of the assessment process.

The aim of this appendix is to give practical and constructive advice on what makes TBT good from the learner's perspective, and to show how the ideas expressed in this book can be applied in practice. I recognize that there are many technical—usually software—constraints to design, but I am, to a large extent, ignoring these. Learners should not have to make adjustments to compensate for poor design, however it is caused. This appendix, therefore, sets out what I believe are the things we should aim for when producing TBT.

## A definition of good TBT

I have been asked many times for my views on what makes good TBT and I often answer this question by saying:

Good TBT motivates, and enables learners to learn what they want to learn, or are required to learn, so that they acquire the knowledge, skills, attitudes and behaviour that the TBT was designed to generate.

People have told me that this is a 'cop-out', and that what they really want to know is how to produce TBT that achieves the above aim. This is, of course, quite a different question, and one that I have tried to answer in this book.

I feel that it would be helpful to look at the question of what makes good TBT by taking a different viewpoint from the one normally held by the TBT designer. I want to look at TBT from the viewpoint of learners, and show how we can evaluate the quality of TBT from their perspective. This is what this appendix sets out to do.

I have tackled this in two parts. First I have looked at what learners need when they come to use a TBT programme and, second, I have looked at how these needs can be met by thinking about TBT in 'output' rather than 'input' terms.

Because of the intricacies of designing and building TBT, designers often lose sight of the outputs of the program they are creating. Sometimes we even lose sight of the purpose of the program. I hope that taking a different view of what learners want will provide some insight and guidance for TBT designers.

## What learners want from TBT

It is possible to look at the wants of learners in ten separate categories:

- ease of use
- clarity
- interest
- choice
- freedom
- help
- fun
- ways of assessing progress
- accuracy
- involvement

### Ease of use

The way in which learners start to use the program, i.e. the process of loading the program, should be easy, with nothing more to do than to load the disk, which should then load the program automatically. People forget, or mistype program names, so this should be done for them to make things easy. Helpful information on how to use the program and simple signals for user action should be built into the program. Navigation within the program should be clearly stated and easy to follow. You might even consider a simple flow chart of the segments of the program. This could show the navigation and the places where options are available, as well as a learning map.

### Clarity

Everything in the programmes should be crystal clear. This includes text, graphics, video, exercises, games and simulations. Text should use simple words and short sentences, and upper and lower case rather than all capitals.

Graphics should add impact and provide a learning point, not just a pretty picture. Before using graphics ask yourself: 'What will the learners learn from this?'

This emphasis on learning should also extend to video, exercises, games and simulations. While interest is important, it has to be related to the learning that is taking place. If learners lose the context in which they are learning, they quickly lose interest or become distracted and stop learning.

### Interest

The first question that TBT designers should ask themselves is: 'Why are people choosing to learn this material?' This is the starting point of their interest. If the reason is negative, e.g. 'I have to, but I don't want to', then maintaining interest is more difficult than when people actually want to learn from the programme. The way to maintain interest is to use a simple formula that works like this:

- Generate interest and curiosity.
- Present a problem for solution.
- Provide information, and help if called for.
- Offer ways for learners to solve the problem; in particular, provide scope for exploration and experimentation.
- Provide one or more possible solutions with explanations.
- Generate a new point of interest and curiosity.

This cycle should be repeated approximately every five or ten minutes. During the cycle learners should be offered as much interaction and choice as possible (and pressing the 'enter' key or the space bar to move forward is *not* interaction). A simple linear approach to TBT does not generate much interest, nor does it provide much opportunity for people whose attention span is short and who want to get on and do something. So learners must have some choice about what they do next.

*Choice*
As people learn in different ways, TBT designers should try to offer scope for them to choose *how* they want to learn. Some might want to go straight to the problem and try to solve it using trial and error (experimentation and exploration); some might like to study information before going to the problem; some might even want to see the solution first, then go back to the problem and see how the solution was arrived at; and yet others might want to take a careful, guided step-by-step approach to reach the solution.

The program design should allow for this level of choice and make it possible for learners to flit around the program, taking a bit from here and a bit from there, before putting it together in their minds.

*Freedom*
Because we learn in different ways, we learn best when we have the freedom to learn the way we want to learn. This can be met partly by providing choice, but choice can be offered within a tightly structured program, that, in effect, provides little or no freedom. Offering a look at segment two before segment one is choice, but if I can't look at the solution to segment nine, or any other segment, then I don't have freedom. There is no point in designers saying that the structure should be logical and follow a certain path, because this probably relates to the way they learn, and we know we all learn differently. Freedom allows learners to do what they want with the program, to use it in any way that appeals to them.

*Help*
One of the best ways to put people off is to offer help that they haven't asked for. One of the traditional ways of responding to learners who give an incorrect answer is to let them try again and/or provide the correct answer.

This is a very poor learning strategy. A much better way would be to ask a different question or present a different problem, and offer learners an 'on request' help facility. We use, and learn from, help when we've asked for it. So allow learners to ask for the solution if they want it—don't presume they will want it and give it to them, anyway.

*Fun*   Learning should be fun. It might not be fun all the time, and sometimes it can be quite scary, but fun is a funny thing. Many people enjoy scary but safe situations, and being uncomfortable, as long as they can end them when they wish. The dictionary defines fun as 'enjoyment, pleasure, amusement', but it is more than this. It is something to do with challenge and achievement, with problems and solutions, with taking risks, with exploring and experimenting, and with being allowed to make mistakes and to learn and grow. This is the fun that should be built into all learning programmes.

*Assessing progress*   We all like to know how well we are doing when we are learning anything new. This should not be in comparison to others in a competitive way, although some people have been conditioned to judge themselves in this way. It is rather to do with knowing that we are moving forward and learning what we have set out to learn. Conventional TBT often seeks to do this with pre- and post-testing. This may have a value, but I doubt it. It is more likely to introduce a threat and a pressure that will actually get in the way of free, enjoyable learning. Progress can be assessed by individuals choosing to tackle problems which clearly become increasingly difficult. Rock climbing is easy to assess as all climbs are graded in severity and people move up a grade as they progress. Nobody tests them—they either do the climb or they don't, and they judge their own performance. This is how it should be in TBT.

*Accuracy*   People object, sometimes violently, when they receive inaccurate information about something. This is especially true about learning. There are few things worse than poor performance caused by inadequate and/or inaccurate information given during training. This means that TBT designers have to carry out research diligently and thoroughly in order to make sure that what people learn is accurate. When information is presented graphically it must also be accurate— near enough is not good enough.

*Involvement*   From the very beginning learners need to be involved in the programme. The idea of users entering their names at the beginning is 'friendly', but hardly constitutes involvement. Providing freedom and choice obviously involves the learner, but it is much more effective to enable learners to construct their own problems, or to develop alternative solutions and then test them out. Involvement is much more than answering multiple-choice questions or making selections on a touch-sensitive screen.

**Output vs. input**     How can TBT designers meet these needs in the most effective way? Well, not by regarding what they do as *input* to the learning programme, although this is, of course, part of the process. I would suggest that we need to look at TBT programmes from the viewpoint of 'What is the outcome of my doing this?' If we can put ourselves in the shoes of learners then we might stop producing content-centred programmes and start creating learning-centred ones instead. If we take this different viewpoint we are likely to find that interest, involvement, fun, etc. come as a natural consequence.

I believe that the 'output' approach is quite easy to adopt. Instead of looking at the content of a programme and trying to sort out how we can best present it to learners, we look at the learning that needs to take place and determine ways that we can help this to happen. So we produce learning-centred programmes that concentrate on outputs, i.e. learning, rather than inputs, i.e. subject matter content. Of course, we still need to present the subject matter, but we can now do it in relation to what has to be learned. Here is an example of what I mean.

---

Office staff in a refinery needed to learn about the fire safety procedures in use. Part of this was presented to them via an interactive video. During the programme they were asked to learn which extinguishers were used for which types of fire. There were five different types, all colour-coded, and a lot of information about which was for what. The results of a short test at the end of the programme were always poor. We reviewed the programme and changed the viewpoint. We asked what was the output of the learning. The answer was 'to know which extinguisher to use if there is a fire'. The programme was changed and learners were presented with several scenarios of fires, still using interactive video. Now when they saw a fire on the screen they had to select an extinguisher from the five coloured symbols. The result of their selection was presented with a scene of the fire going out, or whatever would have happened if they had used the extinguisher in practice. Learners could play with this until they had tried every combination. They quickly and effectively learned from the new programme which colour to use for what fire.

---

When we look at learning from the 'output' viewpoint, it changes our perspective and helps us to produce really imaginative TBT programmes, which are effective because they give learners exactly what they need to learn well. And this is always the final judgement of what constitutes good TBT.

**A sample assessment of technology-based training**     This part of the appendix presents an assessment report that I prepared for a large multi-national bank. The three programmes assessed had been produced by different people. Two by the bank's own staff and one by an outside contractor. The three programmes were (the names are fictional):

- **Advanced Products Support Units**  This was a programme for introducing new staff to this special unit of the bank which gave branches

| Programmes | Advanced Products Support | Workstation Keyboard | Eastern Data Centre |
|---|---|---|---|
| *Learners' needs* | | | |
| • Ease of use | | | |
| • Clarity | | | |
| • Interest | | | |
| • Choice | | | |
| • Freedom | | | |
| • Help | | | |
| • Fun | | | |
| • Assessing progress | | | |
| • Accuracy | | | |
| • Involvement | | | |
| | | | |
| *TBT methods* | | | |
| • Screen layout | | | |
| • Use of colours | | | |
| • Use of graphics | | | |
| • Games | | | |
| • Puzzles | | | |
| • Structure | | | |
| • Interaction | | | |
| • Navigation | | | |
| • Challenge | | | |
| • Exploration and experimentation | | | |
| • Practice | | | |
| • Monitoring learning | | | |
| | | | |

**Figure A.1**  *TBT assessment matrix*

advice and information on a number of special products not normally dealt with at branch level.

- **Workstation Keyboard**   As its name implies, this introduced new staff to the keyboard which they would be using on their workstations.
- **Eastern Data Centre**   This was to introduce staff to the work of the central data centre for the Eastern region of the bank.

The assessment was prepared to determine the quality of the work from both the internal staff and the outside contractor, with a view to either producing more programmes in-house; sending more programmes outside for production; or improving the skills of the bank's staff. The report is presented in three sections: (1) a general overview of the assessment criteria; (2) a report on the three programmes, and (3) specific comments on each.

### Overview

The criteria used for the assessment cover both the learner's needs, and the TBT methods used. These are scored separately on the assessment matrix. Each element is rated out of ten—10 being excellent and 0 being rubbish (or poor, if you prefer).

An explanation of the learner's needs is contained in the first part of this appendix—'A definition of good TBT'. The following explanations are for the TBT methods where I felt there was a need for more information.

### Structure

The structure of the programme will be rated highly if it is flexible and provides considerable freedom for the user to move about from one part to another. In addition, the structure must make it possible for learners to return to wherever they were when they decided to wander.

### Challenge

The challenge I am talking about must come from the way the subject matter is presented, and not from trying to learn from an inadequate structure, i.e. learners should be challenged to learn, not challenged to use the programme.

### Monitoring learning

This rating measures the extent to which the programme monitors the way that learners use it, how they perform in the various exercises, etc. and the extent to which it is possible to extract a performance report.

### Overall product

The assessment matrix in Fig. A.1 shows the ratings for each of the three programmes covered by this report. Where ratings are particularly high or low, further comments are provided. These comments are intended to help the designers to see ways in which the programmes could be improved. However, it should be realized that they are the views and comments of a single reviewer who has his own particular likes and dislikes about how TBT should be produced.

The ratings on the matrix should be related to the scale below to give some view of the overall quality of the programmes, in relation to the criteria shown. Later in this report, I give a personal view of the quality

| Programmes | Advanced Products Support | Workstation Keyboard | Eastern Data Centre |
|---|---|---|---|
| *Learners' needs* | | | |
| • Ease of use | 5 | 9 | 6 |
| • Clarity | 7 | 8 | 6 |
| • Interest | 8 | 8 | 7 |
| • Choice | 4 | 5 | 5 |
| • Freedom | 4 | 4 | 5 |
| • Help | 7 | 5 | 6 |
| • Fun | 4 | 6 | 3 |
| • Assessing progress | 5 | 7 | 5 |
| • Accuracy | 8 | 9 | 8 |
| • Involvement | 4 | 9 | 3 |
| | 56 | 70 | 54 |
| *TBT methods* | | | |
| • Screen layout | 6 | 9 | 8 |
| • Use of colours | 6 | 8 | 6 |
| • Use of graphics | 5 | 10 | 8 |
| • Games | 0 | 0 | 0 |
| • Puzzles | 2 | 0 | 0 |
| • Structure | 6 | 7 | 6 |
| • Interaction | 3 | 8 | 3 |
| • Navigation | 5 | 6 | 7 |
| • Challenge | 7 | 6 | 6 |
| • Exploration and experimentation | 2 | 1 | 2 |
| • Practice | 0 | 4 | 0 |
| • Monitoring learning | 0 | 0 | 0 |
| | 42 | 59 | 46 |
| | 98 | 129 | 100 |

**Figure A.1**  *Completed assessment matrix*

of learning that took place. This is a much more difficult area to assess as people can learn from the most atrocious training materials if their motivation is high enough.

|  | Very poor | Poor | Fair | Good | Excellent |
|---|---|---|---|---|---|
| Learners' needs | <20 | 30 | 45 | 60 | 75+ |
| TBT methods | <25 | 35 | 55 | 65 | 85+ |
| Overall | <45 | 65 | 100 | 125 | 160+ |

On this basis I rated the programmes as follows:

- Advanced Products Support Units      *Fair*
- Workstation Keyboard      *Good*
- Eastern Data Centre      *Fair*

Learning success varied as indicated by the scores in the Learners' needs section of the matrix, but I learned from all the programmes. I learned most effectively from the Workstation Keyboard programme, and then next from the Advanced Products programme. I think this was because of my interest in finance. I learned least from the Eastern Data Centre programme, probably because I was just not interested, and it was so easy to flick through. My interest was never grabbed by a game or a puzzle. I went through the three programmes at different times in order to avoid unfair interference from tiredness or boredom. I was never bored with the Workstation programme, but I became a little bored with Advanced Products and very bored with Eastern Data Centre.

## Specific comments

*Advanced Products Support Units*    The use of graphics throughout is poor, with more emphasis on trying to make the screen appear interesting than as a basis for learning. I found the passive moving graphic at the start annoying. The structure of the programme was not bad, but I would have liked to be able to go back to the menu from wherever I was at any time. A flow chart of the structure of the programme would help.

**Welcome to the team**    The use of graphics to display the team was unnecessary, and the figures were all men. The graphic sequence on interest was poor from a learning perspective—I wondered what was going on.

**Structure of company**    The separate blocks representing each department are okay, but I found the mixture of text and graphics messy.

**Mortgages**    Not being able to get out of sequence is annoying. I didn't think the flow chart worked. Separate flow charts for each transaction might be better.

TESSA    The flow chart doesn't work because it is messy and does not relate directly to the information given. Good responses to incorrect selections.

Unfortunately, the disk I worked from did not let me examine the special products stage.

## Workstation keyboard

A good piece of TBT, with good interaction. The big advantage is that we are using the device to learn about the device, the best way to use TBT. The colours and minimal use of graphics is a model for other TBT designers.

Using pale blue to highlight keys on a blue keyboard is not very clear—yellow or green might be better. I like the consistent use of colours throughout the programme.

The programme is sequential with little choice, except by selection on the main menu, but this doesn't seem to affect the learning.

Easy to follow and easy to learn from. The use of the 'enter' key symbol to indicate 'continue' is good.

I liked this programme very much.

## Eastern Data Centre

This programme has a high level of information for the learner to remember. I have only a disk so I don't know whether there is an accompanying workbook, I think there should be.

I found the use of pressing 'enter' to add a sentence to a screen of text really patronizing. I can cope quite well with a full screen of text. The level of interaction is very poor. The programme is primarily a page-turning exercise, although there is some option about what to do next.

As a learner I was not involved in the learning process except in a passive sense. In fact, it became very easy to 'switch off' and start pressing 'enter' just to get through the programme. Motivated learners will go through it all—but what will they learn, and how can they assess their progress?

The choice of what to do is good. The graphic menu for the departments with the ✔ for when learners have completed them is good. It helps navigation and use of the programme. The presentation has interest and is colourful. It has obviously been a struggle to make the subject interesting in a page-turning programme with little interaction.

**Introduction**   After the first exercise on using the dictionary, I am told: 'You have now completed the exercise on using the dictionary.' I know, I know, I know. Such comments are patronizing and annoying.

**Using the keyboard**   Using different colours for each of the sets of keys highlighted is pretty, but could be confusing. The use of the cursor keys, especially to put the cursor in the box, is hopeless. I tried to go along the line using the move-right cursor, but it jumped all over the place.

**Orientation**   When I am looking at 'The Company' information, only Wester and Retail Warehousing have graphics. Why not all of them? If you start giving learners pretty pictures they come to expect them. Having gone through all the groups I have to choose another to get the selection menu. When numerical data is used in text, make it the significant few, e.g. £4500m, not £4,500,000,000.00. I also found it odd that there was no job description for input/output assistants.

**Security**   On an early screen I am offered the choice of using the dictionary or continuing. If I continue I get some more sentences added to the screen. I re-read the screen every time. Why not give the dictionary option at the end of the screen? The 'door' operation has no short question before information is given—all the others do.

**Receipt and despatch**   Receive runs: the jumping plastic bag does not help learning. I wondered what was happening. It is irritating that someone thinks I might be 'entertained' by, or need, such graphics.

**Statements**   Again the graphic is pointless and, though pretty, does nothing to help people to learn.

Letters arriving: the same pointless use of graphics.

**Some ideas**

Use graphics to present information, not just to produce a colourful display. When developing the programme, concentrate on a mixture of media that allows the learning to be explained, rather than on the presentation of a lot of information—this becomes dreary in spite of the graphics, which are soon taken for granted.

Develop more interaction—here are some ideas:

* Play a game of getting into the data centre to find a yellow envelope.
* Present learners with a problem to solve that requires knowledge of the working of each section of the data centre.
* Display a crossword for learners to complete with the clues being questions about the data centre.
* Provide a workbook with a wide range of exercises, puzzles, problems, etc., the answers to which are in the programme.

# The TBT assessment process

The process of assessing TBT should be divided into three components. The first of these is the learning that actually takes place; the second is the learner's viewpoint; and the third comprises the more technical aspects of designing and building TBT. This part of the appendix describes each of these three components and comments on their importance.

## Learning outcomes

The first, and perhaps the most important, measure of good TBT is whether or not the intended learning actually takes place. However, even if the learning does take place, it may do so only through the diligent struggles of the learner. As we can learn in extremely difficult circumstances, and from the most inadequate materials, it is an insufficient guide to TBT quality to say that the learning occurred.

Some other measure of learning must be added, such as:

- Was it easy to learn?
- Was the learning enjoyable?
- Did the learning take place quickly?
- Did the learning take place without confusion, recap or ambiguity?

In other words, what is important is the quality and process of learning that took place, not just the achievement of learning objectives.

**The learner's viewpoint**

The second part of the assessment process should deal with the way the learner saw the programme. The elements of this are listed in the TBT assessment matrix set out in Fig. A.1. They concentrate on aspects of learning that relate to how the learner perceives the learning that is taking place.

The viewpoint of learners is very important in assessing the way in which the programme has been designed. If the programme is content-centred, i.e. concerned with covering the subject matter in a logical way without reference to the context in which learners will receive the information, then the learners will find it hard to learn. If the programme is learning-centred, i.e. puts the needs of learners first, and presents information in a way that learners can understand in relation to their own experience, then they will learn quickly and easily.

To do this means giving choice and flexibility in the way learners use the programme, depending upon their own individual needs and learning styles, and allowing them to assess their own progress.

**Technical aspects**

The third area of assessment is concerned with how the designer has used the facilities offered through TBT to produce a good learning programme. This is perhaps the easiest area to assess, even though it will vary according to the particular preferences of the reviewer. I like to see very simple programmes with the emphasis on the learning points, rather than on the use of the facilities for the sake of producing a 'flashy' looking programme.

The primary purpose is for people to learn. Entertainment might be part of this, but when entertainment takes over I think the result is nearly always inadequate learning.

There are always constraints presented by the particular hardware and software involved, and these must be known and understood by the reviewer. I have seen excellent programmes produced with the most inferior facilities and, conversely, the height of rubbish with the very best facilities.

**The assessment process**

I believe that the process should have three stages, dealing with each of the three elements of the assessment. The first step should be to play the programme and assess it purely from the learning viewpoint. Reviewers will simply decide whether the programme they have completed has provided the intended learning and, if so, how effectively.

The second stage is to go through the programme again pinpointing those aspects, both good and bad, that assisted or hindered learning. I do this using a notepad ruled down the centre. On the left I write the good things, and on the right I note the bad things. I do this section by section of the programme, then at the end I complete the TBT assessment matrix.

Finally, I go through the programme a third time and look at the specific TBT methods that have been used. I use the same ruled notepad approach, and at the end I sum up using the matrix.

This approach enables me to assess the programme in an integrated way, and yet enables me to be honest in my assessment. By taking the learning viewpoint first, I am, I believe, dealing with the most important issue first; then I look at the second most important, i.e. the needs of learners, and then finally the least important aspect, which is the technical one. In this, I differ from many people who believe that, if a programme is technically good, it must also be good to learn from. I have too much experience of technically superb programmes that do not work to believe this.

Perhaps the best way to assess a TBT programme is to ask people who have no knowledge of TBT to assess the programme from a learning point of view, and then to assess it from the view of the needs of the learner. They would complete only this part of the matrix. Then ask TBT designers to assess the programme from the technical viewpoint, and to complete the technical part of the matrix.

Whichever approach is taken, the end result is to try to assess a TBT programme for its overall training effectiveness, and this means deciding whether the intended learning has taken place, and in a way that motivates learners and is an enjoyable experience. This is the view I take of assessment.

# Index

THE BUSINESS OF TRAINING
Achieving Success in Changing World Markets
Trevor Bentley          ISBN 0-07-707328-2

EVALUATING TRAINING EFFECTIVENESS
Translating Theory into Practice
Peter Bramley          ISBN 0-07-707331-2

DEVELOPING EFFECTIVE TRAINING SKILLS
Tony Pont          ISBN 0-07-707383-5

MAKING MANAGEMENT DEVELOPMENT WORK
Achieving Success in the Nineties
Charles Margerison          ISBN 0-07-707382-7

MANAGING PERSONAL LEARNING AND CHANGE
A Trainer's Guide
Neil Clark          ISBN 0-07-707344-4

HOW TO DESIGN EFFECTIVE TEXT-BASED OPEN
LEARNING:
A Modular Course
Nigel Harrison          ISBN 0-07-707355-X

HOW TO DESIGN EFFECTIVE COMPUTER BASED
TRAINING:
A Modular Course
Nigel Harrison          ISBN 0-07-707354-1

HOW TO SUCCEED IN EMPLOYEE DEVELOPMENT
Moving from Vision to Results
Ed Moorby          ISBN 0-07-707459-9

USING VIDEO IN TRAINING AND EDUCATION
Ashly Pinnington          ISBN 0-07-707384-3

TRANSACTIONAL ANALYSIS FOR TRAINERS
Julie Hay          ISBN 0-07-707470-X